M000165029

Getting Older
Growing
Younger

Barbara Cartland, the world's most famous romantic novelist, who is also an historian, playwright, lecturer, political speaker and television personality, has now written more than 370 books and sold more than 370 million over the world.

She has also had many historical works published and has written four auto-biographies as well as biographies of her mother and her brother, Ronald Cartland, who was the first Member of Parliament to be killed in the last war. The latter, with a preface by Sir Winston Churchill, has just been republished with an introduction by Sir Arthur Bryant.

Love at the Helm, a recent novel, was written with the help and inspiration of the late Admiral of the Fleet, the Earl Mountbatten of Burma. This is being sold for the Mountbatten Memorial Trust.

In 1978 Miss Cartland sang *An Album of Love Songs* with the Royal Philhar-monic Orchestra.

In 1976, by writing 21 books within the space of a single year, she broke the world record, and has continued to do so every year since then with 24, 20, 23, 24, 24, 25 and 22. In the *Guinness Book of Records* she is listed as the world's top-selling author.

In private life Barbara Cartland, who is a Dame of Grace of the Order of St John of Jerusalem, Chairman of the St John Council in Hertfordshire, and Deputy President of the St John Ambulance Brigade, has fought for better conditions and salaries for midwives and nurses.

She has championed the cause of old people, had the law altered regarding gypsies, and founded the first Romany Gypsy camp in the world.

Her designs *Decorating with Love* are sold all over the USA and in 1981 the National Home Fashions League made her 'Woman of Achievement'.

Barbara Cartland's Romances (book of cartoons) has been published in Great Britain and the USA.

Romantic Novels
over 350, the most recently published being:

The Unbreakable Spell	*Revenge of the Heart*
Diona and a Dalmation	*Bride to a Brigand*
Fire in the Blood	*Love Comes West*
The Scots Never Forget	*The Island of Love*
The Rebel Princess	*Theresa and a Tiger*
A Witch's Spell	*Love is Heaven*
Secrets	*Miracle for a Madonna*
The Storms of Love	*A Very Unusual Wife*
Moonlight on the Sphinx	*The Peril and the Prince*
White Lilac	*Alone and Afraid*
The Dream and the Glory	

(in aid of the St John Ambulance Brigade)

Autobiographical and Biographical

The Isthmus Years 1919–1939
The Years of Opportunity 1939–1945
I Search for Rainbows 1945–1976
We Danced All Night 1919–1929
Ronald Cartland (with a Foreword by Sir Winston Churchill)
Polly My Wonderful Mother
I Seek the Miraculous

Historical

Bewitching Women
The Outrageous Queen (the story of Queen Christina of Sweden)
The Scandalous Life of King Carol
The Private Life of Elizabeth, Empress of Austria
Josephine, Empress of France
Diane de Poitiers
Metternich – the Passionate Diplomat
The Private Life of Charles II

Sociology

You in the Home	*Etiquette*
The Fascinating Forties	*The Many Facets of Love*
Marriage for Moderns	*Sex and the Teenager*
Be Vivid, Be Vital	*The Book of Charm*
Love, Life and Sex	*Living Together*
Vitamins for Vitality	*The Youth Secret*
Husbands and Wives	*The Magic of Honey*
Men are Wonderful	*Book of Beauty and Health*

Keep Young and Beautiful by Barbara Cartland and Elinor Glyn

Cookery

Barbara Cartland's Health Food Cookery Book
Food for Love
Magic of Honey Cookbook
Recipes for Lovers
The Romance of Food

Editor of

The Common Problem by Ronald Cartland (with a preface by the
Rt Hon. the Earl of Selbourne, P.C.)
Barbara Cartland's Library of Love
Barbara Cartland's Library of Ancient Wisdom
Written with Love, passionate love letters selected by Barbara Cartland

Drama

Blood Money
French Dressing

Philosophy

Touch the Stars

Radio Operetta

The Rose and the Violet (music by Mark Lubbock), performed in 1942

Radio Plays

The Caged Bird: An Episode in the Life of Elizabeth Empress of Austria, performed
in 1957

General

Barbara Cartland's Book of Useless Information, with a Foreword by
The Earl Mountbatten of Burma (in aid of the United Colleges)
Love and Lovers (picture book)
The Light of Love (prayer book)
Barbara Cartland's Scrapbook (in aid of the Royal Photographic Museum)
Romantic Royal Marriages
Barbara Cartland's Book of Celebrities
Getting Older Growing Younger

Verse

Lines on Life and Love

Music

An Album of Love Songs, sung with the Royal Philharmonic Orchestra

Film

The Flame is Love

Cartoons

Barbara Cartland's Romances (book of cartoons) has recently been published in the USA and Great Britain, and in other parts of the world.

Getting Older Growing Younger

Barbara Cartland

DODD, MEAD & COMPANY

NEW YORK

This book was produced by
Multimedia Publications (UK) Ltd

Text copyright © 1984 Barbara Cartland
Compilation copyright © 1984 Multimedia Publications (UK) Ltd

Published in 1984 by Dodd Mead & Company, Inc.
79 Madison Ave, New York, N.Y. 10016
Published in 1984 in Great Britain by Sidgwick & Jackson Ltd.

First Edition

Library of Congress Cataloging in Publication Data

Cartland, Barbara, 1902-
  Getting older, growing younger.

  Includes index.
  1. Middle aged women – Health and hygiene. 2. Aged
women – Care and hygiene. 3. Youthfulness. I. Title.
RA778.C21794 1984   613′.04244   84-4089
ISBN 0-396-08372-2

Printed in Spain by Graficromo SA, Cordoba

CONTENTS

Most of the products mentioned in this book are available from the Health and Happiness Club, Smithbrook Kilns, Horsham Road, Cranleigh, Surrey GU6 8JJ, England, and from Healthfood Stores both in England and America. Product names are the same in Britain and America unless otherwise stated.

Diane de Poitiers, who was 18 years older than her lover Henry II of France, and kept his adoration until he died, bathed every day in cold water.

She also refused the rich dishes that were popular at the Court of France and preferred fresh fruit and vegetables.

She was so lovely that everybody who saw her was certain she must be a witch.

THINK YOUNG

1

Strangely enough, it was the rebellious Christina, Queen of Sweden who abdicated and shocked all Europe, who said: 'To live and to die beautifully is the Science of Sciences.'

Everybody has to grow old; that is inevitable, but with modern Science and modern thinking there are people who, despite their age, appear to become younger year by year.

The most discerning man in New York, with a very critical eye, telephoned me two days ago and said he had just seen Lillian Gish and Claudette Colbert and they both looked 'fabulous'.

No older person will ever forget how entrancing Lillian Gish looked in the film *Birth of a Nation*. Her sensitivity, her sweetness and fragility were like a light in the darkness.

And now at 87, she is still beautiful.

Claudette Colbert, a few years ago, told the secret of her eternal, spiritual fascination. When a columnist asked her: 'What keeps you looking and feeling so young?' She answered: 'Not worrying about looking and feeling so young!'

She is now 76 and she also explained why her marriage to an ear, nose and throat specialist lasted for 32 years.

'A wife', she said, 'should not bore her husband with her petty ills. He never knew what picture I was in from one year to the next.'

Last year I was on Katie Boyle's *This Is Your Life* television show. Among her other friends I found Evelyn Laye, whom I had not seen for ages. At 83 she looked wonderful and was still acting. How beautiful she was and how brilliantly she sang in *Bitter Sweet*, both in New York, where she stopped the show night after night, and later in England.

Today she still has that charisma which is ageless.

When in 1978 I sang *An Album of Love Songs* with the Royal Philharmonic Orchestra, I said to my producer Norman Newell: 'All I want is to be able to hear myself when travelling in a very fast car!'

The only two singers I can hear at over 70 miles an hour are Frank Sinatra and Perry Como. Their elocution is marvellous and so is their appearance. At 66 Frank Sinatra has a benign look and his blue eyes still twinkle beguilingly. While at 71 – the seventh son of a seventh son – Perry Como's records are both romantic and relaxing.

I have said in my Will that his rendering of *I Believe* is to be played at my funeral.

Looking over the world one can find many people whom 'age has not withered'. When I first visited Jaipur and its Pink Palaces in 1958, the Maharajah and his wife Ayesha, acknowledged to be the most beautiful woman in the world, were like two people out of a fairy-tale.

Today the Rajmata, at 64, still has a loveliness which is as haunting and irresistible as the East. Hers is certainly not just a 'pretty face'. She was the first Maharanee to be elected as a Member of Parliament and she travelled thousands of miles electioneering over sun-baked India in a Landrover. She beat her opponent by 750,000 votes.

She now helps her son, the present Maharajah, to run the Palaces at least one of which has become an hotel and to bring the age-old customs of Jaipur up to date.

In the summer I entertained Queen Farida of Egypt. She has established herself as an artist, and at 62 she has the same beauty and fascinating smile which at 16 made the then slim and handsome 18-year-old King Farouk fall madly in love with her. She told me: 'Ours was a passionate love marriage!' I was so annoyed that I had not put them in my book, *Romantic Royal Marriages*.

Queen Farida bore three daughters before the marriage was dissolved because King Farouk wanted a son. He still loved her so much, however, that he decreed that she was always to be called 'Queen of Egypt'.

'I love like an Englishman, think like a Frenchman, and write like a Russian,' says Peter Ustinov. At 62 his looks, like his wit, have improved with age! It is intriguing to learn that his father was a chef, and his mother a midwife of the Tzars.

What I am leading up to is: What keeps all these people looking young and feeling young?

I remember when I was six thinking that my grandmother was very old. She certainly looked it. Although she was a very handsome woman she wore in the daytime a purple velvet dress trailing on the floor, with a collar of real lace.

I now realize that she was 52 at the time, which today we all of us definitely consider young!

This makes me certain, from my own experience, that age begins in the brain.

When I was a County Councillor for Hertfordshire for nine years, I started, in 1955, making a great deal of fuss about Council Homes. At that particular time, all over England, old people were more or less neglected. They went into Homes which in many cases were converted workhouses, and they just sat and waited to die. There was practically no occupational therapy, no visitors, and of course, very little television to encourage their brain to remain active. Their only occupation was to fight fiercely for their favourite chair, holding it against all-comers.

It was then I realized that age was in the mind, and if one 'thought' old, one became old.

What it really comes down to is keeping your brain active, and taking an intelligent interest in new ideas, new projects and new activities. That is the first stage towards keeping young and repelling the senility of which we all, if we are honest, are afraid.

Earl Mountbatten of Burma used to say to me over and over again: 'I don't want to live so long that I become useless.'

What I think was at the back of his mind was the haunting horror that he might one day become like that great and famous man Sir Winston Churchill in the last years of his life.

I knew Sir Winston first in 1922 when his brain was like a chamois jumping from rock to rock and whenever he was at a party he activated everybody else. In fact, as I have said of so many different leaders, when he came into a room, the tempo rose.

All his life, until the last few years, he had the marvellous facility of making people around him feel more alive as they responded to his magnetism.

I am completely convinced that the only reason in the end why he became a poor, fumbling old man not realizing what was happening around him was that his doctor – as he acknowledged later in his biography – gave Sir Winston a sleeping pill every night.

When I was in Leningrad in 1978 I went to talk to some scientists, as I always do when I visit other countries, and I asked: 'What are you working on?'

'The brain,' they replied.

'So am I!' I said.

They were very excited because they had women of 90 who were doing a full day's work – and I am sure a full day's work in Russia *is* a full day's work!

At the time they were recommending Vitamin B_{15} combined with Ginseng, which they told me was fantastic. I was so impressed I persuaded the scientists in England to make up the same formula when I returned home.

I am quite certain that in Russia the women who were being treated did not receive and could not buy the millions of tranquillizers, sedatives and sleeping pills which are more or less forced upon the public in Western countries including, to a certain extent, America.

Last year we, the tax-payers in Britain, spent £40,000,000 of the money that went to the National Health Service on diazepam (under the brand-name

13

Wife of King Zog, who proclaimed himself King of Albania in 1928 and fell in love with her when he saw her at the Opera on a State Visit to Hungary. Here she is pictured with her son King Leka on the occasion of his marriage to Miss Cullen-Ward (centre) in 1975.

'Certainly from my point of view all depends on health, physical and moral, not talking of the spiritual part, which helped me, by the Grace of God, the most in my life.

If one feels serene one sees it in one's whole demeanour and face!

Physically for me the very best is glasses of clear water in the early morning and night, and the wonderful existing vitamins, then extremely important gentle exercises, respiratory etc., in the morning and a good hour's walk or golf every day.

I now take SOD [Superoxide Dismutase] and GEB [a mixture of Ginseng and Vitamins E and B] every morning, and in between I have Selenium [mineral]. When I have been swimming about ten minutes every day I really feel quite a strong person again, thank, God!'

Valium) alone. With this figure we could have bought four jet fighters for our safety and freedom.

I answer 10,000 letters a year from all over the world, and a very great number of them beg me to tell them how to 'get off' (as they put it) diazepam, chlordiazepoxide and nitrazepam (marketed in the UK as Valium, Librium, Mogadon) and a whole range of drugs. These, they tell me, seem to be making them feel more apathetic, more depressed and more nervous than when they first started taking them.

This is the terrifying effect of sedatives, and many are also accumulative and addictive.

I must add one thing: I have never known a doctor tell any patient that all these drugs ruin and inhibit one's sex life.

I get pathetic letters from women saying they have been very happy with their husbands and although they were getting older they were always able to make love continually and satisfactorily, until suddenly it has stopped.

I find the alteration invariably comes from the fact that one of them has been given a tranquillizer of some sort by the doctor.

All tranquillizers and sedatives kill sex!

This, I believe, is something that should be publicized so that everybody is aware of it.

While I am talking of things that affect the brain, I must mention that Aspirin, which is so freely publicized on the television, can be just as dangerous as any tranquillizer. One of our famous Statesmen had a bleeding ulcer which came from taking too much Aspirin. Overdosage can also cause a loss of hearing, and undoubtedly encourages kidney stones.

Also women often say to me: 'I can't think what is happening! My hair is getting so thin, and I have a bald patch on the top!' Sure enough, they are taking Aspirin, which in my opinion seriously affects the amount of Vitamin B and Vitamin C in the system.

Actually, taken in large quantities during pregnancy, Aspirin can produce a deformed child, and yet very few people are told that!

In just the same way, we have only recently learned that smoking can affect not only the person who smokes, and give them lung cancer, but also the people with whom they come in contact – their wives, their husbands, their children and even those who share an office with them.

This information is now reaching the general public, and women who smoke while they are pregnant have seen on television the terrible dangers to the baby's growth, health, and even life. They should be aware that 2,000 new-born babies died in Britain last year because, among other things, their mothers smoked during pregnancy.

All these dangers are something that our brain has to understand and absorb.

There is in fact so much for the average person to remember in their efforts to keep young and healthy in a world that has been polluted by chemicals, that it is quite difficult to realize the dangers we all of us run every day.

Thank goodness Preventive Medicine has suddenly come to the fore. When Prince Charles praised it in a speech the other day I was so thrilled because to me it has been a personal fight. At last people are beginning to realize the difference Preventive Medicine can make to the ordinary person who wants to keep well.

None of us really wants to live to be over a hundred, but we do want to 'live young', and that is possible if, to start with, we 'think' right.

Scientists have been telling us for years that we use only 10 per cent of our brain, and it is possible to make one's brain improve and enlarge every year that one lives. For the brain to be active, the body must be active too, and this is where the old-fashioned idea that 'Granny likes to sit by the fire knitting', or that 'old people need peace and quiet', is a lot of nonsense. *No way!*

What old people need are interests, and it is fatal to let them think they are out-of-date, unwanted and an encumbrance.

In Italy and other European countries the family is a unit. It has always interested me when I travel through France to see that on Sunday, in every restaurant, even the most expensive kind, you will see the family having their weekly outing. There are father, mother and children of all ages, *and* the grandmother and grandfather are there too! But it is not only on Sundays that they are an inseparable part of the family. They live together, they work together, and they are united by love.

In England it is the opposite. Granny and Grandpa are pushed to one side, and it is not only the old men and women who sit in Council homes who are seldom visited or not at all. It is the same throughout our society.

If a son inherits an ancestral mansion, his widowed mother is consigned to the Dower House, or today more often to a small cottage, and is more or less forgotten.

It is so difficult to alter traditions and therefore all I can say to those who have grown older is: 'Think about yourself and make a life of your own by finding a niche where you are wanted and where you will be appreciated.'

When I look around at the enormous number of people I know all over the world, I find it is not those who are rich who are happy, it is those who are *working*.

The busiest people have always been those who seem to radiate a joy of life, which the French call *joie de vivre* and which is something which is not confined to the young but to those who have developed their brain.

Joie de vivre comes from the brain, and of course, the heart. It is a capacity for enjoying everything, big or small, around you; it is an appreciation of beauty and, I think too, a gratitude for being alive.

So few of us, when we thank God for the big or small mercies that have been accorded us, remember to thank for Life itself – and what could be a more wonderful gift?

When some people look up at the stars and think that each one may have other planets like our own, it makes them feel small and insignificant. But I think actually that if there are billions and billions of other people living in an enormous hemisphere, then it is a privilege and a delight to think that I am one of them, and we share one thing in common: the Life Force that can never die.

There is no such thing as death! How can there be? It is only the shedding of a worn out 'suit of clothes' which we call a body, and the life within us goes on to find another one.

I believe in reincarnation for the simple reason that it is the only thing that can possibly justify the continuing existence of life, and the fact that in nature nothing is lost or wasted.

How was it possible otherwise that Mozart could play the violin perfectly at the age of five, and compose a concerto when he was six that is still performed today?

I love the story of the man who approached Buddha and said to him: 'How many lives, Lord, have I ahead of me?'

Buddha was sitting under a banyan tree, which bears more leaves than any other tree in the world. He looked up and said to the man: 'As many as there are leaves on this tree!'

The man replied: 'So few? How wonderful!'

I think that is an example of what one should feel about life; that we have so much to do, so much to learn that each existence is more rewarding than the last.

It is obvious, therefore, that the most precious, the most wonderful and the most valuable thing we possess is the body. It is only through the body that we learn and advance both spiritually and mentally.

The body is the most intricate, the most fantastic and the most ingenious machine ever created. And yet how badly we treat it! It is extraordinary to me how little care people take of their bodies.

I do not mean going up in an unsafe aeroplane, fighting in wars, or drinking before driving a car, but in ordinary everyday life people treat their bodies far worse than they would treat any vehicle they owned.

18

And yet, knowing its value, knowing how much it means to each one of us personally, we take no trouble to learn about the workings of the body and its needs, but just take for granted that it is there!

The body is, of course, activated by the brain: the most important part of us.

And so we get back to what I have been saying: – that the brain is the first thing we must consider, study and understand if we wish to keep young.

We should not say someone is 'young in heart', but 'young in mind', for that is what counts.

I have two slogans in my life. One is YOU BECOME WHAT YOU THINK.

The other is YOU ARE WHAT YOU EAT.

Because I want you to study these two things very carefully I am going to divide them up into a way that I hope is easy to read and understand.

This is your guide, not to living as long as Methuselah but to living young, looking young and being beautiful both inside and out.

Cleopatra bathed in asses' milk, used a
mask made of honey which kept her
complexion radiant, and improved her
hair with a recipe made of a hare's foot,
some date-stones and the hoof of an ass.

Doctors can show you pictures of the brain and explain to you at great length how it works, how it varies in different people and different nationalities, and of course how it evolved in prehistoric times.

But what we are concerned with at the moment is *your* brain, the Power House of your body and the use *you* are making of it.

As I have already said, I am quite convinced that the people who keep young and happy are those who are active, and who are – to put it in one word – *working.*

By that, however, I do not mean turning a screw in a factory, although that undoubtedly may help, but working at all the mass of things which I find accumulate and increase as one grows older.

My mother died when she was 98½ and she drove her car up to the age of 95. She would not have stopped driving then if she had not fractured her leg, and we refused to allow her to drive again after that.

With her it was not just a question of getting into the car having had it brought to the door. She lived in the country with only one elderly maid to look after her, so it was she who fetched the car from the garage, she who cleaned it, and she who drove it every day, because she was always so busy doing something to help other people. If she was not visiting those who wanted to see her, or assisting them in one way or another, she used to take apples from her trees in the garden to those she knew were ill or who would appreciate them. *Twofold – for the giver & the receiver*

Before she died she was President or Chairman of a dozen different Committees, concerned with charities or institutions, like the Boy Scouts, in which she took a special interest.

I have never known anybody so active or so alive, and at her funeral the church was filled not with big expensive wreaths, but with little bunches of flowers from people whom she had helped in one way or another, and who could not afford anything bigger.

She was a person who was full of gaiety despite the fact that she had more tragedies in her life than any one I know. Soon after she married, her enormously rich father-in-law – my grandfather – lost all his money, my father was killed in the First World War, and both my brothers were killed at Dunkirk.

My mother said something then that I shall never forget. 'If crying could bring them back,' she said, 'I would weep my eyes out, but as it is, I must go on working for other people.'

That really is the answer for those who grow old and think they are unwanted.

No one is ever unwanted.

There are always people who have worse troubles than ourselves; people who need our advice and the wisdom which comes with years. Perhaps more than anything else, people who want us to listen to them.

It is very difficult to generalize, because everybody's life is different, but I have found the people who do the most for others are not the rich, because any fool can write a cheque if they have money in the bank, it is those who *give* of themselves.

And one of the most rewarding things about getting older is that one has more to give.

You may think that is untrue, but experience is very valuable and without even realizing it as you grow older you do become wiser and know more. I find myself asking: 'Why do you expect me to know about this, or that? It is something it seems unlikely I should know.' But because I am so old, things come to my mind or I have heard about them. So that is one way in which one is really needed.

I sometimes receive letters from people saying: 'I can't think what to do with myself. I am alone, unwanted, and I just sit in the house thinking how miserable I am!' I long to give them a good shake and tell them they are being very stupid!

Every Town Hall in the country has a list of different organizations – political, charitable, and those that are just there to amuse. I have never found an organization anywhere which wasn't only too delighted to have a willing helper.

So when people write to me I say: 'Join every organization. You will make new friends, meet new people, and when you have decided which ones you like the best, then you can forget the others. It is not a very difficult thing to do.'

How fortunate older women are today that they can find careers for themselves at any age.

I was brought up to be married, because at the beginning of the century when I was born there was really nothing a lady could do if she was not lucky enough to 'catch' a husband. Even to write was considered *outré*, and Elinor Glyn came in for a lot of criticism, apart from the fact that her story of a Balkan Queen who received her lover lying on a tiger skin was considered very shocking. It sold over 5 million copies and Miss Glyn was invited to stay with the Tzar and Tzarina in St Petersburg where she wrote a novel with a Russian background.

To return to the difficulties of a lady being occupied. There was, for those slightly less exalted, the choice of being a governess or companion for the elderly. But for the so-called upper classes, the latter was the fate of the unmarried daughter who became a slave to the whims of her mother and of course was unpaid.

No one suffered from this position more acutely than King Edward VII's daughter, Princess Victoria – unmarried, shy, sensitive but intelligent. Queen Alexandra, beloved of the British public because of her beauty and their disapproval of the King's unceasing infidelity, was firmly convinced that her daughters had no right to lives of their own.

After much procrastination Princess Louise was married, then Princess Maud, the youngest, found a Viking Prince and later became Queen of Norway.

Victoria was forgotten until unexpectedly a fascinating older man, the 5th Earl of Rosebery, who was Prime Minister, aspired to marry her. He had wealth, power, position, intelligence and charm, but as he was a widower he was lonely.

Queen Alexandra would not consider such an alliance. She had no intention of losing her attentive companion of whom it was said: 'Poor Tora is just a maid to her mother.'

In the long, frustrating years which followed, Princess Victoria grew plainer, bitter and waspish. Her mother remained gloriously lovely to her dying day. Occasionally the Princess would talk of Lord Rosebery, who never remarried, and her voice would break as she said: 'And we could have been *so* happy.'

My mother's elder sister was an 'old maid', and as children we disliked her because we thought she was always criticizing us and finding fault. I was grown up before I learnt she had been extremely pretty when she was a young girl, and had fallen in love with a young soldier. He approached my grandfather for permission for them to marry, only to be told that they would not have enough money! She never had another offer! She lived a dull life in attendance on my grandmother until she died, and then it was too late to do anything on her own.

She was well educated, quick-witted and could, today, have found something interesting to do. But there were no doors open for a middle-aged unmarried woman in the past.

So many people I know started being active when they were quite old.

One friend, a widow, took up cooking when she was 50 and found her children did not want her continually with them. She cooked for different organizations, including businessmen's luncheons, and of course, bazaars and charitable events. Eventually the story had a happy ending because at a business conference she met a charming man who decided she was exactly what he was looking for in his life, so she has remarried and is very happy.

Even if romance does not come into it, one can make new friends, find new ideas and certainly keep busy, which is the most important thing of all. It may even turn out to be extremely rewarding financially.

Another friend of mine was an excellent gardener. She had no money, and therefore could not afford to have much of a garden herself, but she used to go round and advise other people what to do with theirs, whether big or small.

At first she did it for nothing except her expenses, then she became so much in demand that she was able to charge quite a sizeable fee for her advice.

I do not think there is one woman old enough to be a granny who has not accumulated in her life enough experience to be able to advise other people, whether it is on doing up a house, arranging a party or even making special things which other people find impossible to buy in the shops.

I must also cite an example of resourcefulness in a man. He was a big business tycoon who had to retire because he had heart trouble. He was bored to tears! So he thought of the idea – it was new in those days – of a polythene cover for hayricks because thatchers were very hard to find. He sent letters and leaflets to farmers – and in the first year he made £100,000 profit!

And, talking of enterprise, a story I always enjoy recounts what happened before the War when a friend of mine was staying with Sir Otto Biet, who was a millionaire. When she was leaving, the butler said to her: 'I wonder, Madam, if you would do me a real kindness and buy some sweets my young daughter has made?'

'Of course I will, Shaw,' my friend replied. And she bought a box of peppermints and recommended them to her friends.

The girl who made them was Elizabeth Shaw, whose delicious chocolates and peppermints are now to be found in every smart confectioner's!

What it all comes down to is that where women are concerned – and this can affect men in the same way – they are no longer letting themselves become atrophied, they are not letting their brains begin to rot away, which is what actually happens to our brains if we do not use them.

One is never too old to begin!

Einstein started working on atomic nuclear fission when he was 71. Sophocles wrote one of his last great tragedies, part of the *Oedipus* trilogy, at 90 and Titian was only about four years younger when he painted one of his greatest

A great beauty, daughter of the late Duke of Tamames, great-niece of the Empress Eugénie and of the Vicomte de Lesseps, builder of the Suez Canal. President of the Spanish Red Cross. Very active and glamorous.

'My life is very simple. I am Chairman of the Nurses and Hospitals of the Spanish Red Cross and I believe that when you try to help suffering people and you forget about yourself, it's the best way to keep mind and body able to lead an active life.

And don't forget that "early to bed and early to rise makes a woman healthy and wise"!'

masterpieces *The Pietà*.

While I am talking about the brain, I must refer to the ridiculous belief that when you get old you find it hard to sleep, and you therefore need a sleeping pill.

This is *so* dangerous. I cannot stress too often that sleeping pills, like tranquillizers, seriously affect the brain and if you take them in quantity you may become nothing more nor less than a vegetable.

People who tell you that they cannot sleep and therefore must 'take something' are not only destroying themselves but they are afraid of being alone with their thoughts. No one has ever died through not sleeping, and later I will tell you how to sleep by taking honey.

But first, I want to say that if you really cannot bear a few hours of wakefulness, then you ought to be ashamed of your lack of intelligence.

Sleep is certainly a great blessing – but at the same time I find night is the one time one can think clearly without interruption and, to put it briefly, do a little mental 'stock-taking'. Of course all the irritating little things that happened today and tomorrow creep in, but if you are sensible you will put them on one side and do what Napoleon called 'closing the cupboards of the mind'.

Then think about yourself as a person; about your life; about your future, not only in this world, but in the next.

The Church has for centuries recommended that one says one's prayers at night, and this is a way of lifting the heart and the mind from trivial things to more important ones. If you 'Lift up your heart', you will find it easy then to feel closer to the spiritual than at any other time.

I wrote a book called *I Seek the Miraculous*, which is really a 'do-it-yourself kit' for getting in touch with what is called the Supernatural, or if you prefer, the Divine.

I find it tiresome when people tell me they have communicated with those who have 'passed on' through a woman who lives in a London suburb and has a Red Indian Guide who does not speak good English.

I have wanted to get through myself, and I have succeeded.

In *I Seek the Miraculous* I put down all the esoteric experiences I have had, especially in India, and for that matter in many other parts of the world.

Such experiences can happen to each of us every night, if we wish it. Just as a television set is quite useless unless you switch it on, so concentration, meditation and prayer will switch on the spiritual if you wish to do so. This is tremendously rewarding once you realize it can happen, and it is something which is entirely up to you to accept or refuse.

Instead of saying: 'I cannot sleep and must take some pernicious sleeping-pill,' just lie back, close your eyes and lift up your heart, or rather your mind, towards things higher than yourself. Nine times out of ten you will find that after a little while you go to sleep, or else you will discover that the hours spent that way are the most rewarding you have ever experienced.

Of course it is also true that a great deal of sleeplessness comes from indigestion. People eat the wrong things, and those which disagree with them, because they have not studied their bodies properly and therefore, whether they know it or not, it is indigestion which prevents them from sleeping.

Everyone, as they get older, should be careful of fruit with pips, like raspberries, blackberries and currants. It is estimated that 40 per cent of people over the age of 50 in Britain and the USA have some form of diverticulosis.

Salads are very difficult for older people to digest at night, and so is veal. Some people are upset by mushrooms but nearly everyone is affected by one thing or another.

Sleeplessness can also come from agitation or worry. Here again, the answer does not lie in sleeping pills which, when you wake up, give you a head full of cotton wool, which makes it very difficult to step back into reality.

I am ashamed to say that when you go into a British hospital, almost the first thing they ask you is which sleeping pill you take, and the nurses bring them round the wards at night, insisting that the patients take them.

One of the reasons why my novels are so popular in hospitals is that they always end happily, and there is nothing ugly or unpleasant in the stories.

When Mrs Billy Graham, the wife of the famous Evangelist – one of the great personalities of America – was in hospital, a friend of mine took her a large number of 'Barbara Cartland' novels. She said afterwards that they were the only thing that kept her from 'feeling pain'.

If they can keep somebody from feeling pain, then they can also keep you from worrying.

I know this is true because nine years ago I had a very serious operation, and very nearly died. Needless to say, in hospital they started to give me injections at night. When I was strong enough to ask what they were, I got the stock answer: 'Something the doctor ordered.'

'I want to know exactly what it is,' I insisted.

'A pain-killer and something to make you sleep.'

'But I have no pain!'

'But you might have!'

'If I am alive,' I told the nurse, 'I will ask for the injection if I need it, and if I am dead it won't matter!'

They put the syringe on the mantelpiece. After six days, when it had collected dust, they took it away.

My sons brought me lots of history books, which I normally love, but

A beautiful, hardworking First Lady, a skilful speaker who campaigned for her husband alone in 41 States and an adoring mother to her three sons and a daughter. She is artistic, intelligent and very compassionate.

'A proper diet and adequate exercise have always been goals in my daily routine, but I find that they are even more important to me as I grow older.

I always eat breakfast, usually cereal and fruit, to start the day right. For other meals, I like a variety of vegetables and simply prepared chicken or fish. I rarely eat dessert or bread, other than whole grain breads that I enjoy baking myself!

Some kind of exercise each day is very important to me whether the time I have is short or long and whether I jog, ride a bike, swim, or go to an exercise class. The time set aside for exercise is my time to relax, to think about something other than the day's pressures, and to gain a new perspective. It does my spirits at least as much good as it does my body.

My life has been full of surprises and challenges, each one requiring me to learn a great deal and to change my old ways of doing things. That growth has kept me young.

I have enjoyed it all – and look forward to more.'

because I was feeling so ill they seemed too difficult to understand. I had taken into hospital a large number of my novels to give to the nurses, instead I read them myself. I found that because they were happy stories and everything ended exactly as I wanted it to, I 'fell asleep in the arms of the Duke', and recovered far quicker than the doctors had expected!

Apart from taking my honey recipe, which is guaranteed to make you sleep, I suggest therefore you also have a 'Barbara Cartland' by your bed, and read the last five pages. If you cannot get to sleep after that, tell yourself a story in which everything ends happily, whether he is a Duke or not!

Now I am going to ask you once again to think about your brain and ask yourself if you are exercising it.

Are you really using it to its fullest capacity?

Is there not something on which you are 'missing out', but which your brain would appreciate if it had the chance?

I remember when my mother was 83 she told me she was learning to make gloves at the Women's Institute meetings, and I said to her: 'Good Heavens, Mummy! Why do you want to do that?'

'It might come in useful,' she replied. 'One never knows!'

If you can feel like that at 83, I can tell you that you are very young.

Being young is absorbing every bit of knowledge that might come in useful. There is so much one does not know; so much left unread, unseen, un-thought-about in every one of our lives. What I feel is that I have to hurry up and learn it all before my body wears out and my spirit has to move.

I mean that in all sincerity as another story about Buddha will explain.

> *The Lord let a house of a brute to the soul of a man,*
> *And the man said: "Am I your debtor?"*
> *Said the Lord: "Not yet, but make it as clean as you can,*
> *And then I will let you a better."*

Think about this and the little girl of three who a few years ago was a champion chess player! There was also a small boy in America who at the age of six knew every share and fluctuation on the Stock Exchange.

As Kipling wrote:

> *They will come back, come back again,*
> *As long as the red earth rolls.*
> *He never wasted a leaf or tree –*
> *Do you think He would squander souls?*

Lady Elizabeth Foster had two illegitimate children by the Duke of Devonshire, whom she subsequently married.

It was the sweetness of her nature and the kindness she showed her step-children which made her beautiful long after she had reached old age. In fact her most powerful cosmetic was Love.

We have talked about the brain, and now let us turn to a subject on which we all know a little, but not enough – the well-being of the body.

As I have already said, we treat our bodies abominably. Years ago I remarked – annoying a lot of people – that if farmers fed their animals as badly as the average wife feeds her husband, the RSPCA (the Royal Society for the Prevention of Cruelty to Animals) would take them to court!

The French as a nation are very conscious that food is of tremendous importance, in fact it is reckoned that the average French family spends half its weekly wages on food.

In Britain and the USA, many young wives are pressurized into buying processed food, which has little or no goodness in it, and are also lazy enough to replace fresh vegetables with those which have been mashed, bottled, tinned or packaged until there are no longer any vitamins in them.

By the time you reach 50 – which is the 'old age of youth and the youth of old age' – you ought to realize how dangerous this is, and know that to keep well, let alone to keep young, you must put the right fuel into the machine.

What our bodies need first is protein because that is what we ourselves are made of – 30 billion cells of protein. I have always been told that Cary Grant who, the last time I saw him, looked very attractive and very young indeed for 79, takes a large amount of Desiccated Liver. I take two grams a day myself, because then it is not so important to eat a lot of meat, fish, eggs, cheese and soya flour as it would be otherwise.

Incidentally, this is an easy way to take in protein and the World Health Organization has said that for a man to be a good lover he needs 80 grams a day. As the average helping of roast beef is between 18 and 20, it needs an awful lot of other protein foods to catch up!

At the same time, one can get protein from sources other than meat, which a large number of people when they grow older do not like. Eggs are a marvellous source, so is fish. Soya flour, although I personally find it rather boring, is exceptionally high in protein.

Unfortunately for a great number of people, as they grow older, they have a craving to eat what is described as 'tea and toast', but which actually consists of white bread, puddings, cakes and biscuits. *No – Yes* !

All these things are definitely bad for you, and it is a good thing to remember that athletes who particularly need to be strong and active, train mostly on meat and honey.

I am not going into great detail as to what you should eat because there are thousands of books in the Healthfood Stores that will tell you exactly what is good for you, and what is bad.

If, by the age you are at now, you have not learnt that you must have protein, you must have fresh green vegetables and of course, honey, then all I can say is that you are not really worth worrying about!

What I am concerned with are the new ideas which have really only been developed in the last 20 years.

In 1960 when I helped form The National Association for Health, of which I later became the President, everybody, including the Press, asked me what I wanted it for. 'What's wrong with our food?' they asked. 'What's wrong with our medicines? Everybody is more healthy than they have ever been!'

This was untrue, and it was difficult to explain to them that unfortunately people were not as healthy as they should be (one only had to look at the queues waiting to go into hospital), and that cancer figures were rising all the time. Although in this century we have reduced the incidence of mortality in children, people were not actually living any longer than they did in the past.

What was, and is, wrong?

It is, of course, that everything is over-chemicalized, and the food we are putting into our bodies is not really sustaining us; in other words, one can eat three meals a day and yet be suffering from malnutrition!

So although it's Alice in Wonderland-ish and completely idiotic, we have to put into our bodies the food we really need in the shape of vitamins, which are PURE FOOD.

I am not going to tell you here how much the soil, the sea and the air have been polluted because again you know it already.

The Pure Water Association has for years been telling us of the horrors of Fluoride and tap water, which in my case, because I live north of London, passes over three sewer beds before it reaches me. By the time we drink it it is merely a concoction of chemicals.

I remember Richard Dimbleby, whom I loved, in one of his last television shows held up a glass of water and said: 'I wonder who drank this last?'

It would be amusing, if it was not so serious, that the doctors who refuse to consider Preventive Medicine, claim allegiance to Hippocrates, the Greek Father of Medicine whose oath they take. He believed that nature does the real cures and said: 'He who for ordinary cause resigns the fate of his patient to mercury [chemicals] is a vile enemy of the Sick.'

Rachel Carson was the first person who wrote of the horrors of land pollution, but since then the hundreds of books which come out every year have made very little difference to the farmers. They have also been ignored by the great majority of the British and American public.

Instead we have endless advertisements begging us to eat gooey sweets, cakes made with white flour in which there is no Vitamin E, and tinned products which again have been preserved with chemicals.

In case these things upset you, as they are almost bound to do, there are many advertisements that tell you how you can 'soothe away the pains' which inevitably result from a poisoned stomach.

In this mad world in which, apparently, nobody ever thinks of the human results but only of the money somebody is going to make out of selling such rubbish, to be really fit one has to take pure food in tablet form. It is as easy – or as expensive – as that, but at the moment there is absolutely nothing else you can do about it.

Fortunately, however, some people are becoming aware of the dangers in which we live.

The National Association for Health now represents a business that has risen from nothing to one that has a £300 million turnover every year of which a third comes from overseas exports. This is a tremendous achievement in itself, and when, five years ago, I persuaded Lord Mountbatten to open HELFEX, the Health Conference held every two years which represents everybody in the Health Food trade, the buyers from overseas trebled. Two years ago, when it was opened by Prince and Princess Michael of Kent, so many traders applied from overseas that they could not all be accommodated.

This is one way in which we, in Britain, are helping the world, and we have very able colleagues in Switzerland, Germany and, I am glad to say, France and America.

All these countries are becoming extremely 'health conscious', and the Japanese are with us all the way too.

When I look at my post of hundreds of letters that come pouring in every week (and I do not want any more!), it is thrilling to find so many people who say their whole lives have been changed and their whole outlook altered because they have followed my advice. This is, of course, to take natural vitamins.

In Britain we have the best surgeons in the world, and America has the best hospitalization, but I am convinced that when the World was created there was a natural antidote for every disease.

The Creator made the nettle and the dock leaf, and all we have to do in this day and age is to find the 'dock leaf' to cure the old diseases which are still prevalent, and the new ones which 'spring up' overnight.

Beautiful first wife of King Farouk and now an accomplished artist in New York, Rome, Cairo and Paris.

'The way I keep young is by not thinking about getting old. I always do half an hour's meditation when I get up in the morning and before going to bed. I think that having the ability to clear one's mind is a great help in keeping away the bogey of old age.

I think that I have had no time to worry about wrinkles because of my fight to survive and the struggle to be recognised and to make ends meet.

I do not consider myself a great beauty, but sometimes I think I look marvellous when I have made the effort to dress up and to make up.

I have had many furrows in my life, but I think these have helped me and I am now very happy because I can live my life through my children and grandchildren and I get a great deal of satisfaction in arranging my apartments.

I think I have beaten the bogey of getting old by not having to worry now and by my immense peace of mind. I think that inner peace of mind and the soul reflects in the face.'

At the end of the last century and the beginning of this, millions of people died every year of tuberculosis, which is now practically non-existent. I am convinced that our researchers will find an answer, sooner or later, to cancer, and I believe that it will not come from chemical laboratories but from some natural source that has hitherto passed unnoticed.

Also, we have to ask ourselves whether the tremendous increase of cancer is not due to modern appliances such as deep-freezers, microwave ovens and many other things which seem a great innovation when they appear but which, alas, often have 'side-effects'.

To return to food, those who are growing older must realize that their bodies need as much attention as they give their cars, and far more planning than they expend on their holidays.

I take a lot of vitamins every day because I work so hard. I would not have broken my own world record in the last seven years with the number of books I produced – 25 last year – if I did not take my vitamins.

But I also lead what I might call an 'organized' life, because for the majority of the time I eat sensibly, and I keep my brain extremely active by working on a book every day that I am at home. This means a great deal of research, because I read 20 to 30 history books for every novel I write, and as I travel whenever it is possible I also pick up new ideas from each country I visit, which inevitably ends up as the background for a novel.

Apart from this, because I am now published in every country in the world except China, I have representatives in the shape of journalists here almost every day. With continual television and radio interviews it keeps one, in colloquial English, 'on the ball'! *Keeping busy. bodily & spiritual*

Of course, not everybody can lead that sort of life, but whatever sort of life you do lead, as you grow older, you need pure food which one cannot buy in ordinary shops and supermarkets, and few people are fortunate enough to have the land on which to grow what they need.

And so, because we are all in a hurry, we must go to a Healthfood Store to buy food in tablet form exactly as if we were astronauts going up to the moon and taking our food with us.

In every country scientists are looking for something new, something special which will make people feel well and inevitably look well – the two go together.

I am sure by the time this book is published there will be a dozen more new and exciting developments.

At the end of this volume I am going to give you a list of those I have found fantastic and most effective, and which I try religiously on myself before I recommend them to anybody else.

Wherever I go people come up to me and say: 'I've taken my honey this morning!'

This is because in 1970 I wrote *The Magic of Honey*, which swept the world because at that time everybody seemed to have forgotten about honey. In fact, because I said that honey was an aphrodisiac, the Japanese bought up the world's supply of honey and the rest of us were very short of it. Now we have a great many more Japanese!

People laughed at me at the time, but now athletes take honey instead of white sugar, and although there are still some dissenting voices, in hospitals like the Norfolk and Norwich they use honey on open wounds because they say it heals quicker, is less toxic and better for the patient.

I was very amused when I was introduced by Lord Mountbatten to one of the servants who worked at Buckingham Palace, a very healthy, hearty man who told me he had been there for 40 years and was just retiring.

'You don't look old enough to do that!' I remarked.

'That's because I take your honey every day,' he replied.

It is extraordinary that people don't realize the value of something that is bought so easily. When England was known as 'The Isle of Honey' there used to be beehives in every garden. It is one of the oldest foods in the world and the only one that can be kept for 3,000 years without deteriorating.

One of the reasons my mother lived to be so old was that she had taken honey ever since she had been a girl and ate it every day for breakfast.

What seems extraordinary to me is that hospitals do not give their patients honey! But they supply them with white bread which we know is without vital vitamins or roughage, and very strong Indian tea which contains a lot of tannin.

If honey is good for children – which it is, as it makes them grow stronger than children who do not have it – then it is certainly good for old people. It strengthens the bladder, it soothes their nerves, it helps them sleep and, I am absolutely convinced, contains the Elixir of Youth.

It also contains something else, something spiritual which one needs when one is growing old, and Mohammed knew it long before I did. He said: 'Honey is the medicine for the soul; benefit yourselves by the use of the Koran and Honey.'

Before I get to the things which are good for you, and there are a great many, I am going first of all to put down the things which are bad, those which should never be taken by anybody who has any self-respect and is grateful for being alive.

The most beautiful woman Europe has
ever known and one of the greatest
horsewomen of the world, she had a
gymnasium in her dressing-room.

A special soup made of venison,
partridges, pheasants, chicken and
kidneys gave her energy out hunting.
At night she used a mask on her lovely
faced lined with veal.

4

I have already mentioned the terrifying effects of tranquillizers and sedatives, but as a country, Britain is becoming a nation of drug-takers.

It is no use telling me that 'it's only a little one' and really does no harm, because if you take poison it is poisonous however prettily you may 'doll it up'.

I was talking to a man a little while ago who was telling me that he wanted a divorce because his wife was taking two diazepam (under the brand-name Valium) every day. When I asked him what effect it was having on her, he answered: 'She's not there!'

I don't think the story needs any embellishment. You can work it out for yourself. But remember that everything you put into your beautiful body is a vital ingredient for good or for bad.

One thing many people eat which is dead – and I do not need to tell you that it is ridiculous to put anything dead into something that is vitally alive – is white sugar. To refine white sugar, which in its unrefined state is of course brown, it is washed until the colour is eliminated and with it every vitamin and anything which makes it alive. If you eat a piece of wood it has some life in it, but not white sugar.

Therefore into your body, which we hope is very much alive, you shovel a dead substance that has to be digested. Your body uses up its store of vital vitamins in order to digest white sugar. I do not need to tell you how dangerous this is, or what is the effect.

If you go into any roadside café, you will see long-distance lorry drivers, because they feel tired and feel the need for energy, shovelling spoonfuls of white sugar into their cups of tea. It is not surprising that it is estimated that almost every long-distance lorry driver, sooner or later, will get a duodenal ulcer.

Instead of white sugar what you should use is honey whenever possible, or else Fruit Sugar (Fructose), which you can buy at any Healthfood Store. It is a stronger sweetener than white sugar, so although it is a little more expensive, you need only use half the amount.

I was reading an extremely interesting article in *The Times* the other day which told me very concisely all the things I have been saying over the years – that white sugar is dangerous!

In 1977 a United States Senate Select Committee of Nutrition and Human Needs gave a testimony to the success of treating offenders by diet.

When those in trouble had been placed on a diet containing no sugar, coffee, alcohol, sweets or processed food, it changed their whole outlook on life. And out of 252 offenders who stayed on the diet, not one ever returned to Court. This so impressed the US Naval Correctional Center in Seattle that they crossed white sugar and white flour off their menus. A year later they reported there was a reduction in sickness and in medical needs, and a 12 per cent reduction in disciplinary reports.

Even stronger evidence came from a Professor of Criminology at California State University, where 276 chronic young offenders aged between 12 and 18 were prohibited from ice creams, puddings, cookies, soft drinks and sugar. The results were startling. The number of well-behaved juveniles jumped by 71 per cent. Chronic offenders went down by 50 per cent and the incidence of all anti-social behaviour fell to an average of 47 per cent.

To me all this merely confirms what I have always believed, and I am so glad that quite a number of people are beginning to realize the dangers of white sugar.

Before Gloria Swanson died she brought her sixth husband to lunch with me, a man much younger than herself. He told me he had just written a book about the dangers of sugar and had been amazed when it immediately sold four million copies!

Of course we are all aware that as people get older they crave sweet things and especially those who do not drink alcohol. It is quite easy to take the sweetness you want in honey and as honey is, to my mind, a miracle food, it should also be the food of old age.

Other things that are dangerous are smoking and alcohol. I have already touched on smoking, but I would like to point out that if you smoke from adolescence onwards, apart from the fact that the risk of lung cancer is double that of all the other kinds of cancer put together, you also risk losing your teeth before the age of 30, and nothing is more ageing than that! Smokers may also require skin treatment fifteen years earlier than non-smokers. No woman who smokes has, at over 50, a pink-and-white complexion. Smoking tints the skin, obviously from nicotine, and I look sadly at one of my friends whose skin is now undoubtedly beige – because she had red hair she once had a dazzlingly white skin.

When it comes to drink it is wise to remember that, firstly, all alcohol is a sedative; secondly, it destroys brain cells and affects the amount of Vitamin B in the body; and thirdly, it is a beauty killer, especially gin.

A scientific experiment was carried out using calves' liver and alcohol, over a period of 10 days. Pieces of liver were left all night in various different spirits. Here are the results:

Best Brandy	— Liver untouched
Cheap brandy	— Liver damaged
Sherry	— Liver nibbled into round the edges
Rum	— Liver untouched
Whisky	— Liver badly damaged
Gin	— Liver vanished altogether

Personally, I never drink during the week (when I am working), and only occasionally at weekends to keep company with my sons or my friends. Then I drink a very little champagne, or a very small amount of brandy.

I never touch gin which is a gut destroyer. Rum, although it may not be as bad, is certainly fattening and its effects are cumulative, so it is always wise to be careful in places like the Caribbean where everybody drinks it automatically.

Whisky is anti-sex.

Because every sort of alcohol takes the Vitamin B out of your body, it is therefore very wise, after drinking, to take Vitamin B, either as Brewer's Yeast or another form, before you go to bed.

I remember when I first went to America in 1946 just after the War, an American said to me: 'We have something new here. You can drink yourself silly and if you take two tablets you feel wonderful in the morning!' It was the first synthetic Vitamin B-Complex preparation available to the public, in those days made by Lederle.

Because we had been so deprived of vitamins during the War, when I took some — not because I was 'drinking myself silly' but because I thought it would do me good — I felt so much better that I took some back home for my children.

So in 1955 I wrote my first book on vitamins, called *Vitamins for Vitality*, mentioning my own discovery of the wonderful effects of natural vitamins.

When I think of the small beginning it is so satisfying to know that now, wherever I go in the world, people ask me about health.

Once when I was in Peru, the Prime Minister wanted to see me. He only spoke Spanish but his wife who was Japanese spoke excellent English, and the first thing he asked was: 'Is it true Lord Mountbatten takes your vitamins?'

'Yes, it is,' I replied.

'I want what he takes,' the Prime Minister said.

The most brilliant woman in the world, perceptive, sensitive and spiritually motivated.

'The other day I read of a man in the United States of America celebrating his 100th birthday, who said: "Had I known I was going to live so long I would have taken better care of myself!" That's what I am thinking.

I love honey and keep as active as I can, mentally and physically, and to prevent stiffness of body I don't shirk the small everyday tasks which entail bending, stretching and lifting, even running when I can.

I try almost every day to exercise, even for a few minutes. I have evolved my own system, adopting different types of body movements, including Yoga.

To prevent stuffiness of mind I have learnt to be observant, to find interest and pleasure in all manner of things.

To keep young one must feel young and that means keeping fit. I think it is important to be involved in issues or causes that are larger than oneself or one's personal concerns.

A little girl asked her grandmother, "Granny, are you young or old?" Granny replied: "My dear I have been young a very long time!" '

I gave him GEB6, which I will tell you about later, in Chapter 10.

Six months afterwards a great friend of mine, Sirdar Aly Aziz, who sells millions and millions of pounds of exports for Britain overseas, received an urgent telegram from the Prime Minister saying: 'Send me 50 packs of Barbara's vitamins. I have all the Prime Ministers in South America on them!'

Another thing that is very conducive to ageing is to think ugly thoughts; in other words to hate anyone, to be jealous, envious or spiteful. It has always been said that a woman's character shows itself in her face by the time she's 50. I think that is true, and if you are a hard, aggressive, spiteful person, it will undoubtedly show, however cleverly you may make up.

I believe so tremendously in the power of thought that when my daughter was on the way, I was determined she should be beautiful. I read all the books which said that in Ancient Greece they believed in pre-natal influence, so that in the 'hospitals' in which the Greek babies were born they had statues of gods round the beds, at which mothers looked and hoped their children would be like them.

Personally, I think that is too late. I believe you have to start to think of beauty when you first want a baby, and refuse to look at, listen to or talk of anything ugly or unpleasant.

I remember when my daughter was being born the popular book at the time was *No Orchids for Miss Blandish*. It was sensational because it was what I suppose today would be called pornography.

I refused to read it! Instead I read books that I knew would make me feel that everything in the world was lovely, and I also bought a picture of a beautiful baby with fair hair and blue eyes which I looked at every day.

When Raine was born people who came to visit me said in astonishment: 'Good Heavens! You've had her painted already!' She was, in fact, exactly like the picture I had looked at!

My belief in pre-natal influences came about because of a very strange story.

When I was a débutante, I 'came out' with the most beautiful girl I have ever seen. Her name was Blossom Forbes-Robertson. She was the daughter of the famous actor Sir John Forbes-Robertson. She had classical features and was absolutely lovely, but unfortunately she had a glass eye.

When I learnt that her mother had been acting the part of a one-eyed woman up to the seventh month of her pregnancy, it made me think very seriously about pre-natal influence.

Blossom's eye was not bad or blind, the eye-socket was empty!

Another extraordinary story was that of her aunt, the beautiful Maxine Elliott who, with Ethel Barrymore and Helen Hayes, is the only actress to have had a theatre in New York named after her.

When I visited the Château de l'Horizon at Cannes to meet Maxine Elliott, who was then very old, I saw a very beautiful painting of a Venetian woman as I went in through the front door. Everyone exclaimed when they saw it: 'What a wonderful picture of you, Maxine, in one of your roles!' Actually, it was a picture painted in the 17th century that had hung on the wall of her Mother's bedroom before Maxine was born.

If, therefore, we can so affect our unborn children – and I should add that Raine was very beautiful, as she still is, and was the débutante of her year – obviously we can affect our own looks in exactly the same way.

I have met women in my life who were in all honesty plain. They had bad features and yet because of their personality and character, they radiated a beauty that made one think of them as very lovely.

We never pay enough attention to our vibrations. I think of these as electrons which we give out every time we are talking, speaking or meeting people. All of us have known times when we have met somebody who, for no reason at all and not because of something they have said, repels us. That is when our electrons turn round and go back into us. And yet on the other hand we meet people whom we feel we have known all our lives, or perhaps, as I believe, in former lives.

It is then that our vibrations touch theirs and we know a closeness, a unity which cannot be expressed in words but which is undoubtedly there and is very real.

What we have to do as we get older is to make sure our vibrations give out love, sympathy, compassion and understanding to everybody we meet.

We all know people who have a magnetic quality which makes one confide in them.

Gwen Robyns, the writer who has published so many clever biographies including the beautiful one of the late Princess Grace of Monaco, has this quality. I watch with amusement and amazement as people she has never met before tell her the most intimate and extraordinary things about themselves. She magnetizes it out of them.

I think it is the same quality that Mother Teresa of Calcutta has, which comes, of course, from a deep and selfless love to which everybody responds.

Our vibrations have different ways of expressing themselves.

In my book *Barbara Cartland's Celebrities* I chose people who had the magnetic vibrations of leadership whether for good or bad. As I have always said, had I known Hitler I would have put him in the book. As it was, I put in Oswald Mosley, whom I did not like, and various other people whom I found unpleasant but who were undoubtedly leaders in their own way and had that strange magnetism which is very difficult to explain.

'As one gets older it is essential to remain active both physically and mentally. I suffer from a bad back and as a result I have had to give up riding, tennis and golf but every morning I try to do a few back and some of Miss Craig's exercises and I swim whenever it is possible.

At home in Jaipur I start the day by chewing a small piece of turmeric and a margosa and a basil leaf. This is supposed to be good for cleaning one's blood. In Jaipur I lead a fairly regular life and swim both in the morning and in the evening and I also walk to the stables twice a day.

When I am in London I have regular treatments of aromatherapy at Micheline Arcier. These treatments give me a sense of well-being. Apart from these I have no special fads but I do try not to indulge in excesses. Plenty of sleep and fresh air and many varied interests keep me alert and young at heart.'

Born in 1919 Ayesha was one of the most beautiful women in the world. She married the Maharaja of Jaipur with his fairy-tale kingdom of Pink Palaces. She was the first Maharanee to be elected as a Member of Parliament and travelled thousands of miles in the heat and dust electioneering to win by 750,000 votes over her opponent.

Of course my book was mostly about people who have a delightful magnetism, like Douglas Fairbanks Jnr, whose charm is irresistible and has made him one of the best and most tactful, besides the most handsome, representative in world affairs the United States has ever had.

General Eisenhower had a charm which, more than his ability as a military commander, took him to the top.

Looking back into the past, I suppose Lloyd George, the brilliant Welsh Prime Minister who was a wizard at charming people by his oratory, and holding them spellbound, whether they liked it or not, had an irresistible magnetism.

Today I find that Mrs Indira Gandhi has a personality that is so overwhelming that it either draws people to her, so that they admire and love her, as I do, or else makes them aggressive, like the young journalists who try vainly to tear her to pieces. I am absolutely convinced that her strength lies in her spiritual awareness, which almost all Indians have, of the World Beyond the World, and that in her position she uses the Power that is there for us all, if we have the sense to call upon it.

As I have said, vibrations from the brain can be used in very different ways.

Mrs Thatcher uses her great strength by remaining calm, cool and determined whatever the opposition against her. But she too has a tremendous charm that turns enemies into friends, and which even those most opposed to her find hard at times to resist. She is, however, still too young to appear in this book, although I am quite certain, and I have known her for a long time, that she will develop over the years even more fully than she has already.

I predict that when our history comes to be written, Margaret Thatcher will without doubt be one of the greatest women of this century, or any other.

I suppose nobody can write about charm or great personalities without mentioning the Queen Mother.

I remember her first as the sweet, gentle, unassuming Duchess of York, and when at the age of three Raine presented her with a bouquet I wondered who was the more shy, my daughter or the Duchess.

And it was the difficulties of coping with her husband's unexpected inheritance of the Throne, and of course the horrors of War, which brought out her greatness. It gave her that supreme selflessness which makes her so affectionate, understanding and sympathetic towards everybody she meets. It is extraordinary that one small person should have had such an impact not only on the British nation but on the world. It is again her vibrations and charm that draw people to her like a magnet and make her irresistible to whomever she meets or wherever she goes.

I remember my brother, before the War, saying to me: 'She has so much courage, and because she is so small she makes the tears come into my eyes!' I have always remembered that, although it did not seem very significant at the time.

But the Queen Mother's courage has shown itself so vividly over the years, and she has brought strength not only to herself and to her family but to the nation.

There is no doubt that she is the best-loved person in the land – and that is no exaggeration!

We must all of us use our vibrations, and we can all of us ensure that they go out in the right directions. We can journey, just like somebody who has a superjet, or somebody learning to 'throw their voice', to give of ourselves to everybody we meet and to everybody with whom we come in contact.

What we give is very real, a part of the Life Force, and to do so comes easier as we grow older and wiser. *Wisely, age nourishes the need to give of ourselves. Experience wisely executed is the nourisher. Comes back many times!*

Emma Hamilton was the most beautiful woman of her generation, and captivated Britain's greatest admiral, Lord Nelson.

She practised and exercised for her artistic poses of Niobe, Iphigenia, Mary Magdalene and others.

She also had a number of special lotions and salves made for her in Bond Street, which startlingly improved her skin.

Sir Arthur Conan Doyle, who invented Sherlock Holmes, believed so firmly in the power of thought that he always said that if he walked down the road saying: 'I am the Prime Minister! I am the Prime Minister!' people would look at him and say: 'There is the Prime Minister!'

I asked his son Dennis, who was a friend of mine, if this was true and he said: 'I once asked my father if I said I was invisible whether I would be.'

'What did your father reply?' I enquired.

'He said: "No one would notice you!" '

I thought this was a rather far-fetched theory until I met Lady Mendl.

Lady Mendl, whose husband was Ambassador to France and who as a famous interior decorator was better known as Elsie de Wolfe, became beautiful in her late middle-age because she had a shining quality about her which gave her an aura of beauty. She was, in fact, rather ugly as a young woman, but she had a neat, elegant figure. One day in Paris she met a friend of mine who was running Elizabeth Arden's Paris Salon at that time, and she said to her: 'I am so worried!'

'Why?' my friend asked.

'I am 50 today,' Lady Mendl replied, 'and my doctor says I can keep either my face or my figure. What shall I do?'

She thought for a moment, then laughed. 'My face has always been ugly. I shall keep my figure!'

When I heard the story I was surprised, because I had always thought of Lady Mendl as a very attractive, almost beautiful woman, although she was much older than I was.

I found out the whole secret when, after she was dead, a young man who had been almost like a son to her wrote in his book that Lady Mendl had said to him: 'I was born in an ugly house in an ugly street, the last of five children. I was told I was ugly by my parents. The furniture in the house was ugly too, and I always got the dark meat of the chicken! I used to look into a very clear mirror in my bedroom and I told myself: "If I am ugly, I am going to make everything around me beautiful and create beauty, and my friends will be those who also create beauty!" '

She went on to say: 'I've held to that every day of my life. So I have said to myself – like Dr Coué who advised people to say to themselves "Every day I am feeling better and better" – so I said "Every day I will make my small niche in the world more and more beautiful." '

It was something she achieved in the most amazing manner. She insisted on perfection in the running of her house, and perfection in herself. She covered up or ignored those things in life which age other people. She wore gloves to hide her arthritic hands, she disguised her ageing throat with pearls and jewels. She had a reckless, unquenchable courage, the gift of unwavering friendship, and a young, restless, enquiring mind.

So she became beautiful because it was always there in her heart and soul, and as she grew older it came out for everybody to see it.

This proves very conclusively that you can 'become what you think', and I feel I must give you one more famous example.

If you asked who was one of the most beautiful and sexually attractive Frenchwomen in that country's long history of famous and beautiful women, I would automatically reply: 'Madame Récamier!'

She had a reputation for phenomenal beauty, and yet if you look very carefully at her picture in the Louvre, it shows a tall woman with a thick neck, round shoulders and a nose as big as a man's. She had over-long arms, and large hands and feet, and yet the picture is almost breathtaking in its beauty.

David, the artist, probably fell under the spell of her charm, which he captured for posterity.

People have said that Madame Récamier was the most attractive woman who ever lived. Many of her contemporaries claimed she was the loveliest. But people who knew her intimately do not refer to her physical charms so much as her virtues.

Exiled by Napoleon who was jealous of her political influence, Madame Récamier charmed the great men of her age.

The Duke of Wellington wrote to her: 'I confess, Madame, I am not very sorry that business matters will prevent my calling upon you after dinner since each time I see you I leave more deeply impressed by your charm and less inclined to give my attention to Politics!'

Charles James Fox said she was the only woman he knew who united the attractions of pleasure with those of modesty. Prince Augustus of Prussia proposed to her in vain, and Dumas seeing her for the first time guessed her to be 25, when she was actually 54. Chateaubriand was her devoted worshipper for 35 years, during the last period of which she was blind, had a pronounced stoop and was very frail.

She had as many women friends as men, and as one of them wrote on her death: 'To be beloved was the history of Madame Récamier, beloved for her gentleness, her inexhaustible kindness, for the charm of a character that was reflected in a sweet face, beloved for the tender and sympathising friendship which she awarded with an exquisite tact and discrimination of heart, beloved by young and old, small and great: by women, even women, so fastidious where other women were concerned. What other glory is so enviable?'

I think this shows exactly what the power of thought can do; as in the case of Lady Mendl it can create an aura around one so that people feel it with their senses rather than with their eyes.

What I am absolutely sure of is that one's character, whatever one is like, becomes more and more pronounced as one grows older, and is far more revealing than the traditional 'magic mirror on the wall'. Just as good actors or actresses can project their emotions over the footlights to the furthest corner of a theatre, so it is possible to achieve the illusion of beauty in the eyes of those who look at you.

If you understand the importance of your hidden sources of emotional and spiritual power, then beauty can certainly be yours, no matter what your age or what your mirror tells you.

It is a beauty, like love, that can move mountains.

It is very easy to get into the way of thinking that beauty belongs only to the young. We are brainwashed more or less into believing it, because naturally all advertisements for clothes, scents, cosmetics and other feminine necessities are all modelled by very young and very beautiful girls.

That is not to say that everyone finds youth so irresistible that they cannot find beauty and love with much older women.

The great artists of the world, for instance, have always known better.

The reclining figures by Michelangelo in the Medici Sacristy, regarded as the most perfect nudes of the Christian era, were modelled on women who had each had many children.

Rembrandt saw no beauty in a face until joy, sorrow, experience and sacrifice had given character to the models' lives. He always painted the women he loved into his pictures, and most of them, if one looks deeply at the portraits, are not particularly beautiful, nor do they have good figures.

I am sure it was a Frenchman who said: 'Beauty and youth is an accident of nature. In age it is an art.'

I can think of many women I have met who are far more beautiful in middle-age, and often older still, than in their pretty youth.

To quote the French again, they have always said: 'The Englishman is obsessed with youth; a Frenchman prefers experience.' This is borne out by one of the most beautiful Frenchwomen of all time, Diane de Poitiers, who was 18 years older than her lover, Henry II, and kept him adoringly at her feet until he died in a jousting tournament. Even then, when she was subjected to

Has dedicated herself to humanitarian causes.

'It is my personal view that the body is a temple of the soul and it should therefore be treated with great respect.

The purification of the body is at the same time a purification of the soul. By the right vitamin therapy the blood, which is the river of life, is nourished and the spiritual exercise of purifying the mind of destructive and negative forces which we have to face daily, is helped by the nourishment of and the cleansing of that temple.

My father said: "If anyone throws a stone, give them a piece of bread." Forgiveness plays a great part in this destructive world we live in.

If we can try to remember that every day is a precious gift, we can help to make life richer for ourselves and for others.'

the jealousy and hatred of his wife, Catherine de Médicis, Diane still remained exquisitely lovely and men fell in love with her until she died.

But her young lover was captivated not only by her beauty but by her brain. Diane and Henry had much more than sex to bind them closer and yet closer. They studied, taking turns to read aloud to one another. They learned foreign languages, patronized artists, sculptors and men of learning. They surrounded themselves with such beauty that visitors from other lands gasped in amazement at the treasures of the French Court.

More than two centuries were to pass, however, before Diane gave the world the strangest riddle of her youthful appearance. In 1793 her tomb was opened. On either side of her lay two child corpses clad in the same style of clothes as Diane. One child was estimated to be about six years old, the other eight. There is no question that these children were born to her and Henry II.

Did this lovely Goddess of the Moon, as she was called, know the secret of youth not only as far as her mind and body were concerned, but so that she was able to bear children at the age of 58 and 60?

It is one of the many secrets about Diane de Poitiers that will probably never be discovered, but will intrigue and enchant men and women for all time, as she intrigued and enchanted the King.

One of the most famous evergreen beauties of the next century was Ninon de Lenclos who kept her brilliant brain and her eternal charm until she was 90. When she was 60 a man killed himself when she refused his love because she was forced to reveal that he was actually her natural son.

She was a unique example of a woman who enslaved men with her body. But she set them free by enlarging the horizons of their minds. She also said some very wise things. One was: 'Much more genius is needed to make love than to command armies.' Another, which is very true, was: 'If a man gives a woman money it is proof only of his generosity, but if he gives her his time, it is proof of his love.'

One of Ninon's most devoted lovers was a young man aged 25 who pursued her unceasingly but in vain. Quite suddenly, much to his surprise, she sent for him and said: 'Yesterday I was 80 years old. I wanted to wait until that age before you saw me in dishabille.'

He was captivated to the zenith of adoration.

Ninon's beauty lay in her rigorous self-discipline. She ate plain food but refused the bizarre dishes then coming into fashion, except for oysters. She drank little but water and maintained her physical and mental powers.

Ninon's real monument is not in the classical tradition of French literature, not in the brilliant epigrams of La Rochefoucauld, Saint-Evremond and other dilettantes who worshipped her. It is in the eternal fame of the Frenchwoman as a lover and the reputation of the Frenchwoman as the beloved, whatever her age.

Fifty years after Ninon's death, the philosopher Benjamin Franklin wrote a very remarkable letter to a young man who asked his advice about women. Although it might seem slightly shocking to some people, I think it is worth quoting for the sake of those women who think that to be old is to have lost all their physical charms for a man.

Benjamin Franklin, after proclaiming marriage to be the most natural state for a man, said: 'If a man cannot or will not marry then his love affairs should be with old women rather than young ones, because they have more knowledge of the world. Because there is scarcely such a thing as an old woman who is not a good woman.

'In every animal that walks upright the deficiency of the fluid that fills the muscles appears not on the highest part. The face grows lank and wrinkled, then the neck, then the breasts and arms – the lower parts continuing to the last, plump as ever; so that covering all above with a basket and regarding only what is below the girdle it is impossible to know an old woman from a young one.

'And as in the dark all cats are grey, the pleasant corporal enjoyment with an old woman is at least equal and frequently superior; every knack being, by practice, capable of improvement . . .'

So many women want to be attractive, but they are either too lazy to make the effort or too ignorant.

'Too lazy' is the right way to describe the modern way of not making the best of oneself.

When I left the schoolroom in 1919 after the First World War, there were two million surplus women in England, and because everybody was hard up after the privations and expense of four years of war, chaperons almost ceased to exist. As young people like myself wanted to dance all day and all night, we found that we had the unique privilege – which had never happened before – of being allowed to be alone with a man.

In the last gasp of their authority chaperons, in the shape of our mothers, said that we could go out dancing with a man, if he asked us, but we were not allowed to dine with him unless it was a party of four.

It seemed a very strange restriction, but that was what they insisted upon, and it suited the young men who, having come out of the Services, had very little money. They therefore dined frugally at their clubs and fetched us afterwards to dance until dawn at the night clubs that were springing up all over London.

Because of the shortage of men it was obvious that a girl had to be very

A great English beauty and celebrity.

'I feel it is very important that any regime one chooses must be kept to regularly. For instance, doing a few basic exercises every day is much better than half an hour's violent exercise a week, or spasmodically.

However late I go to bed I am always called at 9 o'clock with a glass of hot water and lemon juice (no sugar) and have breakfast in bed at 9.15 a.m. These fifteen minutes give me time to slap cold water on my face, read the morning's mail and generally wake up.

I never drink anything alcoholic until dinner-time and then only very dry light wine or dry champagne. I hate all hard liquor and I have literally never tasted a cocktail in my life.

I consider swimming the best tonic in the world, but only in salt water – and the colder the better!'

attractive, otherwise she stayed at home looking at the wallpaper.

In consequence, we were very conscious of our looks and it became a self-discipline, whether one was out with a young man or whether one was alone, always to look one's best.

The first thing I do every morning of my life, when I am called, is to get out of bed, comb my hair, powder my face and make up my lips. I do not want anybody to see me until I look neat and tidy, and I remember how one of the most beautiful women I have ever seen, Millicent, Duchess of Sutherland, never allowed anybody to see her before she had put on her false eyelashes – which in those days meant applying them one at a time!

She was another person who was infinitely lovelier when she was over 40 and running a General Hospital in Calais in the First World War, than she was as a débutante. All her patients fell in love with her and my husband, who was one of them, told me that her beauty kept many of the men from dying simply because she inspired them with the will to live.

She was born with beautiful features and she developed as she grew older an inner beauty that one felt immediately on meeting her. She was still gloriously beautiful when she died aged 87. She had an irrepressible desire to miss nothing in life and a gaiety which never failed.

But to get back to taking trouble, I am astonished when other women walk about in the morning shopping or working, without doing anything to their appearance. Then later in the day they dress up and look infinitely more attractive.

Once, when I underwent an extremely serious operation, I was told I was the first patient who had ever been allowed into the operating theatre wearing turquoise eye-shadow! As soon as I came out of the anaesthetic I managed to put on an eye-liner, and when after two or three days I was strong enough to mascara my eyelashes the nurses laughed and said: 'Now we know you are really getting better!'

That was some time ago, and now at last it has been recognized that it is very important psychologically for a woman to worry about her appearance. Nearly every up-to-date hospital encourages women patients to study their faces and to use lipstick as one of the first steps towards getting back to normal.

Taking the trouble is very important to those who have reached middle-age and every year that comes after it.

And one of the things to remember is to 'carry yourself young' because the 'old age slouch' gives away the years you have lived quicker than almost anything else.

Doctors attributed Queen Mary's excellent constitution and the reason she did so much in her old age to the fact that she held herself so well. She always sat bolt upright, which we now know was due to the fact that she wore the tightly-laced corsets that were fashionable when she was young.

But what can be worse for your figure than sprawling about in low chairs and motor car seats which are designed by men to destroy any woman's figure?

Gaylord Hauser, an American, who was one of the first dieticians to teach me an enormous amount about vitamins, has always believed that one of the most important aids to health is a flat, firm stomach.

It is the only exercise he teaches his students and was recommended to him, he says, by Sir Arbuthnot Lane, physician to George V, whom I knew when I was a young girl. The 'Stomach Lift' that he recommended to me, and I am sure still does, although he is over 88 now, consists of pulling the stomach in and up and holding it against the spine. It automatically gives one a good posture, grace, self-confidence and vitality.

Gaylord Hauser said you can achieve a flat, firm stomach in 30 to 60 days and as a result live many years longer than you might otherwise have expected.

You would have thought, after all they have been told about walking lightly and gracefully and the hours they have spent watching film stars, that the young women of today would float over the ground like Grecian nymphs. Instead of which all too often they stump about trying to look like men in trousers – which no woman with any sensibility would wear – and shoes which either have heels that are too high or too low.

It is the age of 'Couldn't Care Less', and this is where, if she is clever, the older woman comes into her own.

Lillie Langtry came from Jersey to London with one black dress in which she conquered not only the artistic world, but also Edward VII.

She had a perfect natural complexion, and she always washed her face in rain water. She also had a special powder named after her which she used herself because she knew it contained nothing harmful.

6

I have said so much about the brain that I feel it is time that we consider the body.

I was talking to a very attractive widow a little while ago and she was telling me about a man she had been seeing a lot.

'Is he in love with you?' I asked.

'Yes, he is,' she replied, 'but there is nothing like *that*! How could I now that I am over sixty? And I cannot bear to think about my figure!'

I knew what she meant and thought it was a great pity that anyone should give up what is one of the most fascinating, delightful things that can happen, which is sex between a man and a woman.

Women have fought since the very earliest times to be beautiful and to keep their beauty. It is unfortunately a battle that is lost in the end – and yet many women have achieved their goal of remaining beautiful to the very end of their lives.

Elinor Glyn is one who concentrated on her very unusual, exotic and exciting beauty and was determined not to lose it. 'There are three things a woman ought to look,' she said. 'Straight as a dart, supple as a snake, and proud as a tiger lily.'

She could be very scathing about other women and once, about Viscountess Castlerosse, the beauty of the Thirties, she said to me: 'She looks like a hungry fox!'

Elinor was all woman, with her green eyes and flaming red hair. Her husband hired a swimming pool on their honeymoon so that she could swim naked with her long hair flowing out behind her.

No one of my age will ever forget the commotion and gossip caused by the rhyme:

> *Would you like to sin with Elinor Glyn*
> *On a tiger skin?*
> *Or would you prefer to merely err*
> *On any old fur?*

She was, however, a great lady. When the Marquess of Curzon, who had been her lover for years, married someone with money and she saw the announcement in *The Times*, she did not complain. She burnt the 500 letters she had received from him and never again mentioned his name!

The Ancient Greeks found beauty in everything they saw and in everything they felt. The Greek mother, we can read, used to pray that above all things her children might be beautiful. It was not the pretty 'Chocolate Box' prettiness that became fashionable many centuries later. The Greek profile was a famous characteristic and the Greek neck was long and always powerful. They believed that a powerful neck was a promise of long life.

In the Venus de Milo we see also powerful shoulders that hardly slope at all.

The truth is that Greek women triumphantly combined grace with health and hardihood. So much did they believe in cleanliness that even the statues of Adonis were washed on Feast Days. You can see on the Greek vases in the British Museum many scenes of male and female figures bathing, and the Greek heroes and heroines famed for their beautiful appearance were often described as taking baths or disporting themselves in a swimming pool. Hector's first action after leaving the battlefield was to take a hot bath, and Ulysses was described as taking a cold plunge in the sea, then having a hot bath.

There is no doubt that baths, cleanliness and cold water have contributed through the centuries a great deal to women's beauty.

The beauty of Diane de Poitiers, whom I have already mentioned, even reportedly defied the grave because those who opened her coffin many years after her death were said to have seen, for a moment, Diane in all her loveliness, as fresh and perfect as she had been when she was alive.

I am sure the reason she was so beautiful was that in an age when no one bathed at the French Court, she took cold baths every day, and ignoring the over-rich food and wine, preferred fruit and vegetables of which today we know the true value.

The Romans of course built their baths wherever they went. You find them in many parts of Britain and all over Europe and this surprising passion for physical hygiene definitely improved their whole appearance.

But Roman women did not only rely on cold water – they took a tremendous amount of trouble over their faces, and as Juvenal says in one of his poems:

> . . . her cheeks as smooth as silk
> Are polished with the wash of asses' milk.

Pliny described how: 'nearly a million a year was drained away to the remoter East, to purchase aromatics and jewels for the elaborate toilette of the Roman lady.'

Nero's mistress Poppaea mixed dough with asses' milk to wear as a mask at night, while another mask made of rice was believed to remove wrinkles.

Mediaeval women, extolled by the Troubadours, were seeking something higher and more ecstatic than the beauty of their appearance. The courtly singers and poets were perhaps the first influence after the Dark Ages to make women realize that their brains were more important than their bodies, and ideals could inspire more effectively than mere physical passion.

Mediaeval women did not, then, take old age lying down! We learn that in summer the perfumes of the rose, violet and lily, and in the winter those of musk, aloes, balsam and the like were thought not only to cheer the heart, but to sharpen the wits, to make the blood course through the veins, and cause the skin to shine.

They also took the bark of peach, elder or holly to help the tongue to speak, to keep the sight clear and fair, and make the arms and buttocks thicker and fleshier.

In simple words they took a great deal of trouble with themselves, and were determined to be the delicate, flower-like women whom the painter Botticelli immortalized.

It seems extraordinary that despite Botticelli's *Venus* rising in a shell from the sea, the Reformation should for a time have banished from Northern Europe everything that was joyous and good, through an overpowering sense of human sin that had to be purged.

Nudity became sinful in itself. It was paradoxically almost a virtue to proclaim one was dirty.

Elizabeth I stored up some of the future suspicion of Popery in the Royal line simply because she had baths put into the rooms at Windsor Castle. The Commentator who wrote: 'She did bathe herself once a month, whether she required it or not,' was not complimenting the Queen but criticizing her lax ways.

Less than a century later when Charles II indulged in some highly questionable revels, including a mock-marriage to the Duchess of Portsmouth at the Arlington residence at Euston, Suffolk, the final proof that the place was filled with 'devilish temptation' was revealed to be the news that the house had a number of bathrooms.

Doctors, through the Royal College of Physicians, officially reiterated Parliament's proclamation during the Commonwealth that baths were dangerous: people's bodies might be clean, but their morals would be sullied.

The fact that almost every beautiful woman in history was known to bathe heightened the suspicion of the Puritans that bathing was immoral. They shuddered at the information that Cleopatra bathed daily in perfumed water, that Messalina had slaves to collect droplets of morning dew from the flowers until there was enough to sponge her body. And the Puritans were prepared

Has a capacity for friendship which means she is never forgotten on either side of the Atlantic.

'Life is beautiful . . . I live on a Shoestring and try to make it look pure gold. God gave me health and laughter . . . and my mother and England gave me the rest.

I am over-sensitive, vulnerable and brought up on FEAR . . . which alas! is my undoing, but this Green and Pleasant Land with its sense of fun and gentle climate keeps one young forever.

Every night I do just as my mother did . . . I wash my face with Palmolive soap and warm water . . . then rub some cold cream into my face before I lay me down to sleep. When I awake in the morning I do the same, then remove the cream and put on a little powder.

So be happy and laugh away the years.

I rise with the lark and sleep with the owl. It's all how you tick. Play with the world and everyone who comes your way will play with you . . . So why grow old?'

to swear that Diane de Poitiers' youthful beauty until she was 60 clearly indicated that she had made a pact with the Devil! It was announced – and believed – at that time that Satan had given her a recipe for the broth made from gold which kept her skin so youthful.

No one for a moment believed her own statement: that the wicked elixir was simply a daily immersion in cold water!

Later famous people, however, continued to 'prove' to those deriding them that there was an alliance between wickedness and bathing.

The notorious Duke of Queensberry was known to bathe every day. Beau Brummell bathed in milk, as did the Princess Borghese, sister of Napoleon. She, indeed, had a young Negro to lift her in and out of the bath in her house in Paris (which is now the British Embassy), so that she could appreciate to the full the whiteness of her skin against his.

It was therefore very disturbing to the remaining Puritans a few years later to learn that the pretty young girl who so unexpectedly ascended the Throne as Queen Victoria, had immediately put in hand renovations and alterations to Buckingham Palace. Hot water was to be conveyed to her apartments and there was to be a portable bath in her bedroom!

In modern times the great wit and journalist Viscount Castlerosse wrote: 'A gentleman takes a bath twice a day, those on a lower scale once a week, and unmentionable inhuman creatures occasionally.'

I am writing all this to tell you that I believe very firmly that cold water is important for the body. Ice rubbed lightly over the face tightens the skin as one gets older and prevents that sagging look which happens to so many elderly women and which no one, however kind, could think becoming. Young women, like ex-Queen Alexandra of Yugoslavia, have long used ice on their breasts which is also very wise, if you wish them to keep their shape.

But the most important place on which to rub ice very gently and keep it moving is, I believe, along the line of the chin. If that is loose, nothing is more ageing and nothing really helps except a face lift which is very expensive and for which nobody who works hard has the time.

One of the good effects of bathing is quite frankly that one is clean, and I notice that both old women and old men sometimes get lax as the years go by. This is really stepping back in time, which is, to say the very least of it, a very regrettable mistake.

And while we are talking of the body: think about your skin.

First your skin should smell fresh and fragrant. All through history there have been descriptions of women whose natural smell was attractive and sweet.

Nellie Fowler, a *demi-mondaine* in Edwardian days, had a natural smell that was so delicate that her lovers would beg her to sleep with their handkerchiefs under her pillow.

But she was an exception. As a general rule older skins do not smell nice without attention.

They also change colour. A white skin has been a sign of beauty in women since the beginning of civilization. It is only today that women wish to be sun-burnt. Nothing is more ageing or produces lines quicker!

Petronius, the Beau Brummell of Nero's day, describes the Roman taste in women, and says: 'her snowy feet within the slender gold-strapped sandals! They would dull the radiance of Parian marble.'

In the Middle Ages in Spain a white skin was prized and there was a reference to 'the uncovered breasts, whiter than crystal'. In Restoration times, the avid writer Count Hamilton describes Mrs Hyde as 'having a skin of dazzling whiteness'.

Lillie Langtry is immortal because she was unique. She walked with Princes but remained herself. Everyone knows the story of how she conquered Society with her beauty and one little black dress. Mistress of the Prince of Wales, she was painted by every famous artist and filled London Theatres when she took to the stage. Americans adored her, millionaires loaded her with gifts of jewellery, 6,000 acres, and a racing stable.

When she was 45 she married 28-year-old Sir Hugo de Bathe, and 19 years later she retired to Monte Carlo. There, as a woman of 75, she was still amazingly beautiful, simply dressed in black and with a *pearly white skin.*

Lord Horne of Stirkoke commanded the First Army in World War I. He married my husband's aunt and on my marriage she presented me at Buck-ingham Palace. She was a very kind woman, but no one could call her a beauty. Dressed up with the three white Prince-of-Wales feathers on her head she looked very impressive, but her skin – because she hunted in all weathers – was like leather. As we drove along the Mall to the Palace she said to me wistfully: 'If I could have my life over again, I have no regrets except that I would take care of my skin.'

The vogue for sunburn was hailed with delight by women with bad, coarse or discoloured skin.

What so many of them do not realize is that once they are tanned really brown, they never go white again. The yellow tint remains and is bad enough on a young woman, but really ugly on someone older.

The sun produces lines. So, to reiterate, do slimming and smoking. Past the age of 40, once the lines are there, it is almost impossible to magic them away.

Only a serene, calm, happy outlook and LOVE may succeed when creams and lotions fail.

QUEEN ALEXANDRA

Dazzlingly beautiful, with an irresistible charm that brought King Edward back to her side however many times he strayed from it, she hid the scar on her neck by inventing a diamond dog-collar, and in her old age she wore a toupee.

She also took great pains to keep the lines from her face with what we now call 'moisturising cream', and she was always carefully and discreetly made up.

When I said that you must think your body beautiful, keep a flat stomach, and walk with grace, the inevitable question is – what do you do if you are fat?

In all the years I have been writing on health problems I have refused to advocate any of the fashionable diets which, in my opinion, are not only extremely bad for one physically, but inevitably make people disagreeable.

It is absolutely ridiculous to think that by starving oneself one can create beauty because it upsets the balance of your body and also the mind.

I remember years ago reading a book in which a man who was a great advocate of Yoga breathing and the spiritual thinking that comes from it, was incarcerated during a war in a Turkish prison.

'Because I found I was incessantly hungry,' he wrote later, 'I found it impossible to raise my mind to spiritual things; my needs were too physical.'

This is exactly what happens when people go on stringent diets and they not only become cross and irritable, but it destroys any aura of beauty that might vibrate from them.

What I have found, and only recently, is the perfect diet, which works, and is so easy that I cannot think why, when I knew about it in the 1930s, I never thought about it again.

A few months ago Sir John Mills, one of England's most brilliant and delightful film stars came to lunch. He had just finished playing the part of the Viceroy in *Gandhi*, in which he looked very distinguished.

I asked him during lunch: 'Tell me, John, how have you such a wonderful figure? It is absolutely extraordinary that a man of 75 should have a completely flat stomach, and not an ounce of extra flesh!'

He laughed and said: 'It is all due to Dr Hay's Diet!'

'Do you mean the Dr Hay we all heard about in the Thirties?' I asked. 'I remember a number of my friends doing it then.'

'Yes,' he agreed, 'and I was very fat at the time. I had a duodenal ulcer and I always felt ill. I went on the Hay Diet, I lost weight immediately, my duodenal ulcer disappeared, and I felt extremely well.'

He then, like every man I have ever known, showed me that he was wearing the same suit that he had bought, I think 20 years ago, and he hadn't altered an inch since his tailor made it for him.

I then looked back and remembered exactly what Dr Hay had said. He was an American and he told us that there were two sorts of digestive juices in our bodies – one to digest starch, the other protein – and the fatal thing is to mix the two because it causes acidity and invariably makes people put on weight.

At my age I am very wary of any form of dieting because just as one ages from the top downwards, one slims downwards, and the first thing that happens is that one gets innumerable wrinkles on one's face because the moisture leaves the skin.

But I did refuse to eat puddings at luncheon or dinner and kept everything that was starchy for tea. I lost 7 lbs without any effort at all and had to take two inches out of my waist-bands. My son on the same diet lost 14 lbs and said he felt extremely well.

It is actually the easiest diet in the world, except that it is rather an effort not to eat toast with your egg at breakfast. Otherwise it is completely 'plain sailing', and I have protein, vegetables and fruit at lunch and dinner, and keep chocolate cake, and meringues for tea.

People just cannot believe, that after all the complicated calorie counting and starvation diets they have tried, that Dr Hay and Sir John Mills should be so successful. But I promise you it does work and one's face remains untouched so that there are no extra lines, no dry skin and no pouches under the chin line.

Also, because it is so easy it prevents one being undoubtedly a crashing bore over some fanciful diet when one's hostess has taken a great deal of trouble to supervise a meal which she hopes you'll enjoy.

I remember when Gloria Swanson came to lunch with me that she was fanatical on how one must eat exactly the right food at exactly the right time. She did not bring her little bag with her as she did on other occasions. But she sat on my son's right at luncheon and he said afterwards that she droned on about food until he was sick of hearing about it.

If you want to be a success, for Heaven's sake keep your special prejudices – and most of all your beauty hints – to yourself!

Nobody else wants to hear them, especially at a time when you should be amusing and paying for your meal by being charming.

Maybe that's a strange thing to say, but it's usually older people who understand that if one is being entertained, and it is quite an effort on most people's part these days, one is expected to 'sing for one's supper'.

A man of 60 said to me the other day: 'I was brought up to believe that if somebody was kind enough to entertain me, I should make some response, and that I have tried to do all my life.'

My grandfather who was a great martinet, used to say to his four daughters and one precious son: 'Talk! It doesn't matter what you say. Talk! No one wants you to sit at the table with a smug face saying nothing!'

'Of course,' my mother said to me, 'after he had roared at us in such a way everything flew out of our heads, and naturally we looked blank, so he abused us again!'

But my grandfather was right. It is very important that one starts very early with one's children to get them to realize that not only with hospitality but with anything else one is expected to 'pay the bill'. Not in cash, but with charm, good manners, and by listening sympathetically.

I think the reason we have such bad manners these days, not only in the home but in the streets, the factories, on the trains and everywhere else, is that women have ceased to be feminine.

It used to be automatic that men of every type and class made themselves polite and pleasant to a woman, because she was a woman.

Cab drivers, and later taxi drivers when I was young, always got out of their driving seat to open the door for a lady; shop assistants called you 'Madam' automatically; and in the country every man and boy you met would either take off his hat or cap, or touch it politely.

It seems to me extraordinary that good manners have flown out of the window with the emancipation of women, and I cannot help thinking it is entirely their fault.

At one time women ruled the world from the pillow and by being a woman.

Sir Henry Savile, a mathematical scholar who died in 1621, put it very clearly: 'Women have more strength in their looks than we have in our laws,' he said, 'and more power by their tears than we have by our arguments.'

American-born Oliver Holmes put it more simply: 'They govern the world – those sweet-lipped women.'

Women have, since the beginning of time, exerted tremendous power over human affairs for good or for bad.

History would have been very different if Cleopatra in her efforts to rule the world, had not influenced first Caesar and then Mark Antony.

History was also made when the behaviour of Lola Montez caused a revolt against King Ludwig I of Bavaria. She sparked off an epidemic of revolutions which spread over the turbulent Europe of 1848.

The Emperor of France was hurled from his throne. His going opened the way for ambitious Russia to take Bavaria. It was the first ominous move which was to make the German Swastika an emblem of destruction and terror across the face of Europe.

Christina of Sweden by her abdication created the first incident in a series of events which shaped the boundaries of Eastern Europe and gave the basic

Descended from the Kings of Ireland and widow of the 5th Duke of Sutherland. He said of her: 'In everything she tackles she throws herself into it, heart and soul.' Has a vitality and natural gaiety which gives happiness wherever she goes.

How true!

'I believe that to keep young it is essential to keep moving. It is people who sit about and who are sluggish who get rheumatism and aches and pains.

I get up early in the morning and have usually left the house by nine o'clock. I have always walked a lot and I drive my car long distances without feeling tired. I eat sparingly and sensibly and I never rest during the day but try to get eight hours' sleep at night.

I do not smoke, and drink very little. I take the vitamins Barbara gives me and I eat honey.'

pattern of Russia which emerged under Peter the Great.

These women were not young girls. They were full-blooded women with beauty and brains in addition to a magnetism which men found irresistible. Men fought against their power even while they succumbed and were conquered. Not by discussions, pacts, laws, or the cry of equality, but because they were feminine women.

The 17th-century dramatist, Thomas Otway, wrote passionately what many men think secretly:

> *What mighty ills have been done by woman?*
> *Who was't betrayed the Capitol? A woman!*
> *Who lost Mark Antony the world? A woman!*
> *Who was the cause of the long ten years war*
> *And laid at last old Troy in ashes? Woman!*
> *Destructive, damnable, deceitful woman!*

A man when he is in love invariably says: 'You have bewitched me.' He cannot believe a woman can make him feel so emotional and that he could lose his heart except by supernatural means.

I think many of the divorce cases happen because after marriage he finds she is in fact, a very ordinary, commonplace young woman with no mystery and nothing bewitching about her.

Only a very bewitching, entrancing, feminine woman can keep a man content in the belief that he was enticed into love because he could not help himself. And who can do this better than a woman experienced in years and wisdom?

Today women are so determined on equality that they become pseudo-men, and all the beautiful things they inaugurated as women have therefore been set on one side.

Lord Beaverbrook once said to me: 'A man is like a peacock who wants to spread his tail before a beautiful woman.'

What women so often forget today is to let the man 'spread his tail' because they are too busy showing off their own plumage. They also forget in their desire for equality that it is ingrained in a man that he must be brave, courageous, that he must protect those who are weaker than himself, and to do so he must be masculine.

But women now emasculate men by putting them into a plastic apron to do the washing-up, and if they keep telling him they are cleverer than he is, they lose what should be very important to every woman, the pedestal on which men have put them since the beginning of time.

That is, if they are the right sort of women and have been worshipped both as a wife and a mother.

'Our marriage crashed because Lorna would never let me show off my achievements,' a very wealthy, 'self-made' man once told me. 'I made my own way in the world, and I am very proud of it. I like to tell somebody what I have done, but Lorna always wanted to talk about herself, so I left her. My new wife is just the opposite; she encourages me to talk and I find a new delight every evening in going home to her.'

In a busy household, in fact in every household where the husband and wife both work, it is very difficult for them to be alone together and be able to talk by themselves.

That is why I advise every married couple to have another honeymoon *every* year if they can. It may be a weekend, a week, or a few days, but they must go somewhere alone, where they need think only of each other.

There is always a granny, and this is where the older woman can help, to look after the children. Then the married couple can go away even if it is only for a couple of nights in a tent if they cannot afford anything more; it will re-create, rejuvenate and revitalize their marriage.

My husband and I spent our honeymoon in Paris and every year we spent a few days there in the same hotel, usually from Friday to Monday. We forgot our troubles, our family, our work. We didn't go to race meetings, to dress shows or meet our friends. We just spent those days together, talking and making love as we had on our honeymoon.

That annual honeymoon made my husband feel masculine, masterful and romantic and it really did keep the 27 years we had together before he died, happy, and perfect in almost every way.

A honeymoon is only effective if a woman is prepared to play her part as a woman. While you must employ your mental powers and capacity to be intelligent, you must also use your female assets.

In the French Assembly great enthusiasm was aroused among the Deputies when during a debate on Sex Equality a speaker finished with the words: 'After all, there is very little difference between the sexes.'

Another Deputy jumped up and exclaimed: '*Vive la différence!*'

Every man dreams of his ideal woman and expects to find her. And while woman dreams of her ideal man, she loves him as he is, with his faults, his failings and his weaknesses.

That is one of the great differences of the sexes.

Because you *are* a woman you have to make yourself part of the shrine that a man has set up in his heart to hold his ideals. You have to fill it to make his dreams come true.

Men, because of this secret shrine are far more idealistic and impractical

Exquisite, unforgettable, she made every dance a poem of beauty.

'Like yourself, I feel that being constantly at work in different aspects of my profession — theatre, TV, radio — keeps one active mentally which is so important, isn't it?

Alas, I don't dance any more, but I firmly believe that dancing has helped to keep me physically active and able to dash from one part of the country to another without being too exhausted!

I do a few stretching exercises, eat and drink in moderation, and try to get as much rest as possible – which isn't easy!'

than they allow, and can be bitterly disillusioned and miserable if the woman they worship shows her frailties or becomes very much 'down-to-earth'.

He will not say so, but he seeks a goddess, and he is always disappointed to find that she is made of flesh and blood.

What a clever woman does is to keep him believing that she is the woman of his dreams; the woman who is the other half of himself; the woman who was made for him and meant for him through perhaps thousands of other lives.

Why should you want to make him believe that you are as good as, if not better than he is, at work, at games, at running the house, in the ordinary everyday difficulties of human existence?

It is the older woman who usually has the good sense to let a man worship her, and so brings out the very best in him.

I always think of Disraeli who adored his wife, although he had been quite a Rake before he met her, and who although she was 12 years older than he was, continued to worship her until she died.

He said to her once: 'Why, my dear, you are more like a mistress than a wife!' He thought her perfect, and what he meant was that she pandered to him in a manner a young woman of today would think scornfully of as 'cossetting'. But theirs was a true love story and one of the happiest marriages of all time.

Not young, not beautiful, getting old and in ill-health, Mary Anne was all woman. As her husband said: 'We are all born for love. It is the principle of existence and its only end.'

Surely that was far better than the modern attitude of 'Anything you can do, I can do better!' – which invariably means that the husband or lover looks around for somebody else to whom like a peacock he can spread his tail!

Her wit, her beauty and her charm captivated the raffish Charles II, but what also held him captive was that in an era when few people washed themselves or their clothes Nell was always spotlessly clean, and so were her petticoats.

She also undoubtedly enjoyed the oranges she sold in Drury Lane.

Those last pages may seem to be for the young marrieds, but they are also very applicable to women in their 40s and 50s who often become very aggressive. This can be remedied by Hormone Replacement Therapy, as I explain later.

One of the reasons English and American women have become so dictatorial and unfeminine is that they are frustrated, although they would never admit it, in that men pay little attention to them as women.

This is really a case of what came first – the chicken or the egg – but there is no doubt, meanwhile, that in France the very air of Paris is magical. Women feel desirable, men feel roguish, and a woman whatever her age is always very feminine with a man.

A Frenchwoman has an extraordinary mixture of allure, appeal and sexual self-confidence that is part of her make-up from the cradle to the grave.

No Frenchman would imply that Brigitte Bardot was getting old, either in words or his treatment of her, and the reason for that relates once more to the brain rather than anything purely physical. Frenchmen expect their women to be intelligent, mysterious, natural, very feminine, and they never lose interest in them as women, whatever their age.

Frenchwomen therefore remain eternally coquettish and flirtatious. One has only to see them in a restaurant flirting with their husbands as if each was a new man in their lives, to compare them with an English married couple who sit staring into space, looking bored as if they have run out of conversation, even about the mortgage and the bank balance.

A Royal Physician once said to me: 'Men are not born wonderful lovers, but women make them wonderful, by telling them continually how wonderful they are.' That is what Frenchwomen do, not only in words, but with their eyes, the way they move and the way they smile at a man.

A famous Harley Street specialist confided: 'My women patients are always telling me that their husbands are too tired to make love to them. The real explanation is that they are bored.'

He continued: 'I said to one woman: "Do you ever arouse his appetite with anything novel or unusual to stimulate his interest?" and she replied: "Oh, Doctor, whatever would he think of me?"'

He went on to say that a man can get tired of anything, however good,

The most loved top British film star whose home life is surrounded by an aura of happiness.

SIR JOHN MILLS, C.B.E.

'I have always believed that diet is the most important factor in keeping age at bay. In fact "old age" can be made to look quite ridiculous.

I am surprised that my ears have retained their normal length, as I am practically a rabbit! I consume about four tons of salad and fruit a day. I eat very little meat, and never eat starch and protein at the same meal. In fact, I am a great believer in the Dr Hay diet.

I also work as hard as I can all the time. At the moment I am playing eight shows a week at Wyndham's Theatre in "Little Lies", which is a revival of Pinero's "The Magistrate". It is an enormously demanding part and needs a tremendous amount of energy.

I am a great believer in honey (the pure kind) and during the Show I have at least two cups of China tea with two large spoonsful in each.'

which is presented to him day after day, month after month, year after year. 'Desire requires imagination,' he said. 'Women get into bed and talk about the price of potatoes, and are surprised when their husbands turn over and go to sleep.'

Feeling romantic on the first day of marriage is easy.

Proving that romance is still flourishing on the five-hundredth day or the thousandth is harder!

I am not suggesting for a moment that the wife who finds that her marriage loses its glamour should try to become a replica of the famous Grecian *Hetaira* – or courtesan – who was treated as a member of the aristocracy in Ancient Athens.

But I do suggest that by throwing off her inhibitions and accepting the delights of love, and giving her husband all the pleasures that her femininity can contrive, she can turn what has become banal into an adventure.

It can in fact, be a thrilling romance whose beauty and satisfaction can eclipse anything which existed in the first experimental years of marriage.

Real love, as I have tried to explain before in this book is distinct from the exciting and passing *affaires de coeur* and takes no account of age, physical attributes or familiarity.

Indeed history has proved over and over again that the maturity of the body needs maturity of experience in the mind, and an older woman can be physically far more attractive to an intelligent man than a virginal juvenile.

What is more, the chance of successful sexual relations is allegedly greater in established married life than between two comparative strangers on their honeymoon.

People talk so much about sex and continue to do so, and most of the books written about it are absolute rubbish, that it is difficult to explain that sex is an Art.

It is actually the most perfect and beautiful expression of happiness that two people can attain together.

Instead of either rushing at it like a bull in a china shop, or being shocked by the whole thing, we have to learn about it as we learn about anything else that is a very important part of one's education.

There is, as we know, a lot of talk about sex education for the young, but far too much time is spent in explaining the mechanics of the body rather than on lifting up the mind.

I remember when it was first discussed in England on television, a woman teacher was shown explaining to a class of children who looked about nine or ten years old, exactly how the sexes got together to create a baby.

When she had finished, and I must say she made the whole thing sound rather boring, a small boy lifted up his hand for attention and asked: 'Doesn't love come into it?'

It was a long time ago, but I have never forgotten that child's question.

What we all have to remember are Byron's love lines, and know they are true.

> Yes, love indeed is light from Heaven;
> A spark of that immortal fire
> With angels shared, by Allah given,
> To lift from earth our low desire.

It seems extraordinary to me that after all the poets, writers and the great thinkers of every age have told us about what love really means, we should let it sink to the low level of pornography which has swept over this country and America rather worse, I think than any of the other countries in the world.

And I am concerned that the moral tone of both nations was lowered because older and supposedly wiser men and women did nothing about it before it was too late.

Have you, as an older woman or older man tried to explain to your people how much they are missing, or rather misunderstanding, the beauty and glory of love?

'I'm too old to understand what my children and grandchildren feel,' a famous American hostess said to me the other day. 'They wouldn't listen to me.'

'Nonsense!' I replied. 'Children keep their parents young.'

This is a cliché, but it's true, and if you cannot unfortunately have any children then I think the people who adopt them are very sensible.

Many of the American film stars find that a family gives them a sense of security and, more important, a background of home.

The every-young, entrancing Bob Hope and his charming wife Dolores, whom he married in 1933, have four adopted children. I am sure they make him funnier than he is anyway, because children are very critical.

My sons, with whom I work, tease me unmercifully – but they want me to be a success and undoubtedly keep me up to the mark.

James Cagney has two adopted children, and lovely film star Irene Dunne has an adopted daughter who is a talented pianist. Once Miss Dunne's political enthusiasm made her cross swords with Eleanor Roosevelt, who said: 'She does know about working and has a warm heart, but she doesn't know a thing about laws!'

It is obvious as your children grow older that they will become more independent and have their own ideas on everything and especially love. But their father's and mother's example is very important and although they may not admit it, of course, you have influenced them since they were in the cradle. Their ideas and ideals of love must come from your love and your ideals.

Disraeli wrote in the last century: 'We are all born for love, it is the principle of existence and its only end.'

Long before him, Shakespeare had said: 'Love is a spirit, all compact of fire.'

Of course it is hard to explain love even to oneself, let alone anyone else. It is a very delicate thing, and it belongs to the brain, as I have already said, but if it is part imagination, it is also part human impulse.

Both are ignited with a god-like spiritual spark which can only come from outside the confines of the body.

There are no words to describe lyric love:

> *Half-angel and half-bird,*
> *And all a wonder and wild desire.*

One can only feel it and go on feeling it with every sense and nerve, all one's mind and heart.

What I think comes as we get older is that we are able to express the Divine Love that is within us better than in our impulsive, hurrying youth.

A short while ago I realized there was no collection of passionate love letters obtainable, with the exception of a book written by that beautiful, clever young woman, Lady Antonia Fraser.

I therefore collected the most passionate letters I have ever read during my research and I was astonished how brilliantly the older men and women expressed their feelings and with a physical passion which must have been quite surprising in those rather restrictive days.

Of course, no one wrote more perfectly of love than the Brownings, and no one had a more exciting or romantic marriage.

The love story of Robert Browning and Elizabeth Barrett is almost immaculate in its perfection.

Robert Browning was, as we know, a middle-aged Romeo, and it is sometimes forgotten that Elizabeth was his real inspiration of romance. She was a fragile beauty, wilting in a repressive sickroom, and from her family's point of view near to death.

How they got to know each other, how they ran away to Italy, how she had a child when she was 43 years of age was all so dramatic and so moving, and yet it seemed to be summed up in Elizabeth's last word when at 55 years old she died in her adoring husband's arms.

It was quite simply – 'Beautiful!'

They will neither of them ever be forgotten, and Elizabeth's love poem written to her husband is what quite obviously every woman, if she is honest, wants to feel.

> *How do I love thee? Let me count the ways.*
> *I love thee to the depth and breadth and height*
> *My soul can reach, when feeling out of sight*
> *For the ends of Being and ideal Grace.*
> *I love thee to the level of every day's*
> *Most quiet need, by sun and candle light.*
> *I love thee freely, as men strive for rights;*
> *I love thee purely as they turn from praise.*
> *I love thee with the passion put to use*
> *In my old griefs, and with my childhood's faith.*
> *I love thee with a love I seemed to lose*
> *With my lost saints – I love thee with the breath*
> *Smiles, tears, of all my life! – and, if God choose,*
> *I shall but love thee better after death.*

You may not be able to write like that but you can *feel* like that, at any age.

I am absolutely convinced that what we need today in the world is more women who glory in the fact that they are feminine and are not ashamed to love a man passionately and adoringly because he is a man.

There is one woman who is doing this already and for whom I have the greatest admiration, and I cannot help feeling I helped just a little to make her what she is – the most glamorous Super-Star in the world: the present Princess of Wales.

When she was a teenage girl – and I first met her when my daughter married her father, Earl Spencer – Lady Diana always immediately read the novels I brought for my daughter. It is no secret that to her and all the girls at her school I was their favourite author.

She is exactly like one of my heroines in that she is not only beautiful, charming, gentle and kind with a compassionate heart, but she also takes the trouble to listen to what people have to say and is never ashamed to say that she herself wants to learn more.

But more than anything else, she has brought back beauty into a world that is sadly in need of it, not only beauty of appearance and face, but the beauty that comes from having a heart and letting the spirit of love glow from her like a light.

That is what we all need, and that is what a real woman in the shape of the Princess of Wales is giving, please God, to a new generation.

Nefertiti, the sensational but unfortunate wife of the Egyptian Pharaoh Akhenaton. She used kohl around her eyes and plucked her hairline to give herself a high forehead.

Inevitably, when one talks about old age one wonders about sex, so let me make it clear from the very beginning why sex between a man and a woman who love each other should continue indefinitely, in some cases until they are over 90!

Again we get back to the undeniable truth that this, like everything else, is to do with the brain.

I am continually pointing out to people that love – which is the most perfect, wonderful emotion possible, and which is actually the nearest thing to the Divine — comes from the imagination, or what you may prefer to call the spirit and the soul.

I am talking about *real* love, not passion, lust or the desire which a man and a woman can have for each other and which flares up like a fire and is as quickly burnt out.

Real love is the ideal love of the poets, the musicians and the artists, and which we all seek because it is the most perfect and ecstatic emotion in the world, peculiar only to mankind.

The act of procreation which of course exists in every living animal, reptile and insect is, as far as we know, something that occurs from a natural impulse and has nothing to do with their minds.

When Man was created, he was given a mind which rose above the physical needs of the body and reached out towards the spiritual. It was then he craved love which he expressed by wishing to protect a woman, keep her as his own and inevitably make her the mother of his children.

Of course there were other sorts of women. Even in the Garden of Eden there was Lilith! But real love which is part of the imagination, the need of the spirit, and the adoration of the soul, is the 'Golden Fleece' which every man in his dreams imagines he will find.

What is so delightful is that this does happen, not once or twice, but to millions and millions of people.

Happiness has no publicity, and unfortunately we only hear about the love that goes wrong, the love that is disappointing, and in this day and age, the love that is perverted, despoiled and degraded into becoming pornography.

Throughout my long life I have known a great number of people who

Fascinating, handsome, courageous and diplomatic.

'. . . I do manage to do quite a lot of things, but possibly the two go together.

In the first place, I watch my weight . . . I do whatever exercise I can get around to doing depending on where I am; e.g. if I am in London I will find a pool, or in the sea . . . I also play tennis when and if an opportunity presents itself.

I also try to walk as much as I possibly can, wherever I am. One, two, three or four miles a day . . . IF – IF – IF!!??

I was born with a natural curiosity and a delight in every waking moment – I don't need artificial stimulants to keep going, as I was always blessed with more than my share of energy, and I resent having to sleep at night because I can't wait for the next day to come along!

I had a fairly sickly childhood, and patches of serious illnesses in my maturity – but on the whole, I have enjoyed reasonably good health.'

were blissfully happy and for whom there were no headlines, no sordid divorce, no recriminations.

It is very easy for people to laugh at love which is idealistic, but I believe they laugh because they are jealous, because it is something they have not found themselves.

And yet in every young person, when they begin to think about love with the opposite sex it is the dream of a love like that of Romeo and Juliet, Dante and Beatrice, and the Troubadours.

Unfortunately, propaganda – or what was called advertisement until Hitler changed it into a weapon of war – has ruined so many young lives by making boys and girls think that the physical satisfaction of sex is all they should aim for.

What we should be teaching them is about the love which lifts human beings from the animal into a likeness of God, and it still exists today, although a number of people are too shy to talk about it.

The love to which I am referring is lasting and does not depend at all upon your age.

I often think of how the handsome, attractive Lord Palmerston when he was 82 and Prime Minister of England, ran up the steps to the 'Ladies Gallery' in the House of Commons at 3 o'clock in the morning so that he could kiss his wife, whom he adored and who certainly worshipped him.

When they married, Lady Palmerston was 52 and a widow, and he was 51, and they were so passionately in love with one another that they remained active lovers to the end of their lives.

Somebody once said: 'Man's first love will make him feel older than he is, his last love will make him actually younger than his years!'

By contrast, there is a very amusing story about the 5th Lord Grantley who, at 87, was cited as co-respondent in a divorce case. The Judge tried to suggest in Court whether the grounds given in the action could be admitted at that age. Lord Grantley listened attentively because he was somewhat deaf. Then he said in a perfectly audible voice to his son: 'You'd think the fellow was suggesting that I'm past it!'

The Decree Nisi was granted, however, to Lord Grantley's great satisfaction.

I have known older people who have been lovers until the same age and older, and I think what they find is that while sex in the last years of one's life cannot be so frequent, it is often infinitely more satisfying.

An older woman once said to me, 'One becomes more grateful for love as one grows older, and one savours it as something very precious and very wonderful!'

I knew exactly what she meant, thinking of how the young take love as their right, and treat it carelessly, as if it would last for ever.

Love whenever it comes into our lives, has to be nurtured, tended and helped to grow.

It is usually the woman who, after she is married, does not struggle to increase her husband's love and treasure it as if it was something very precious.

I was very impressed when Petula Clark, the singer, was asked on television a little while ago: 'Is it difficult having a career and being married to a Frenchman?'

'I *work* at my marriage every day,' she replied.

That is a very good answer.

One has to work at marriage, just as one works at a job or anything else which requires the full attention of our minds and imagination.

I must stress, as I have so often on television, that love or what people today call Romance, is the woman's job in marriage and in life. She is born to look beautiful, give out beauty, and to keep alive the love which is given her, which is, in fact, the beauty of God.

Men are often accused of being the first to become bored in a marriage. In my experience, it is far too often the woman who, if she is not bored, becomes careless to the point of indifference.

That is when a marriage breaks up, and very often the real reason – although it may not be admitted – is that the sexual intimacy between the two has either become humdrum and stale, or else non-existent.

When I was a little girl the most important person in Worcestershire, where I lived, was the Earl of Coventry. He was a marvellous old man, a great character and a great gentleman. He had been Captain and Gold Stick of the Corps of Gentlemen-at-Arms, Master of the Buckhounds, and when I knew him, was the Lord Lieutenant.

He had known the great Duke of Wellington, and he remembered going to lunch with Lord and Lady Palmerston. 'Covey', as he was always known, lived in great style in a magnificent Georgian house where I went to fabulous children's parties.

On the Earl's 60th wedding anniversary someone said to his wife, who had produced 13 children and hunted up to the day before each one was born: 'How delightful it must be for you and your husband to have been such close friends for 60 years.'

'Friends? *Friends?*' the Countess questioned indignantly. ' "Covey" and I have been lovers for 60 years and will be for many years more. Friends indeed!'

It is not hard, if you look, to find people who feel the same today, but it frightens me when I remember that in 1919 when I emerged from the schoolroom divorce statistics in Great Britain were 0.01 per cent of the population. Today in the latest survey it was suggested that three marriages out of four that take place will end in the Divorce Courts.

What is wrong? Quite honestly I think it is that young people today do not have the stamina that their fathers and mothers had to face the difficulties and problems which arise in every marriage.

We also get back to the point that a great number of young women are not feminine enough to keep their husbands happy.

Englishmen in particular are very good husbands, but they are not very voluble lovers. An Englishman does not get up in the morning like an Italian or other members of the Latin race to wonder which women will attract him during the day.

He is thinking about his job, the news in the papers, and of course of sport!

If his home is a happy one and his wife is tender, understanding, gentle and loving, it is very unlikely that he will look elsewhere.

I am absolutely certain in my own mind that this eternal harping on 'We are equal!' is at the root, in a great number of broken marriages which get into the Divorce Courts.

There is a lot to be said for the Edwardian attitude that whatever happens in family life it should never become a public scandal. Of course, there were men and women who lived together in unhappiness and frustration, but there were also far more really happy marriages than exist today.

Love is a very strange emotion, and yet a man will challenge the world rather than lose the woman he loves, and a woman will sacrifice her life for the man to whom she belongs.

It is very hard to define real love, which I think proves itself over the years and is very different, as I have already said, from the transitory passion that can flare up like a match to a can of petrol and die almost as quickly.

What in many ways is far worse than a single act of infidelity, although many women do not think so, is a habitual lack of good manners between a husband and wife, and an indifference which comes from familiarity.

To quote the blissful marriage of the Disraelis again, I often think of what Mary Anne said of her husband after they had been married for many years: 'Dizzy' has always given me love, companionship, trust and good manners.'

This is one of the main foundations for a good marriage.

It is an expression of affection, and here again it is for the woman to see that a man expresses himself in the way she wants to hear.

I often say to young girls who are getting married: 'The best way to make a man say "I love you" is to say you love him. Do not be shy but tell him how much he means to you. Tell him what makes you happy, excited and, of course, passionate. It is very important because if you express what you are feeling, then he will express his love in the same way.'

When I was away from my husband he telephoned me every evening and also always wrote me a letter. Naturally I wrote to him because I enjoyed every one of those letters, which I still have.

Mary Anne Disraeli's letter when Disraeli took office is an example to all those wives who never write to their husbands, or if they do are too embarrassed to put their affection on paper.

She wrote: 'Bless you, my darling. Your own happy, devoted wife wishes you joy. I hope you make as good a Chancellor of the Exchequer as you have been a husband for your affectionate Mary Anne.'

One of a delightful old couple who exemplify everything I have said is a charming intelligent old Canon Lovall, at one time Rector of our Parish Church. He was 92 and his wife was 94 when she died a few months ago. They were so fond of each other and so much in love that when you saw them together, the very air seemed to light up with their happiness.

When I heard that Mary had died very peacefully after what had been a long illness I thought the Canon would be distraught.

He wrote me a beautiful letter in which he said: 'I do not feel unhappy because Mary is with me, as she always has been, and I know she will never leave me.'

I know exactly what he felt because I believe that real love surmounts the grave. Just as there is no death and life goes on, so those who are very close to us stay with us as long as we need them, or until we join them.

I had 27 years of perfect happiness with my husband, although when I married Hugh he was a sick man and I was told I would be very fortunate if he lived for another five years.

At 19 he had been posted to Flanders with his Regiment, the Cameron Highlanders. Two months later he took part in the terrible slaughter at the Battle of Passchendaele. The life expectancy of a Subaltern there was 20 minutes, and on 31st July 1918 there were 279 casualties in the Battalion to which my husband was attached. He was severely, almost mortally, wounded. In attacking the enemy trenches, for which he was awarded the Military Cross, he was hit in the chest by a sniper's dumdum bullet which passed through his right shoulder and out of his back, exploding as it went. This, among other injuries, collapsed his lung and smashed three ribs. He turned head-over-heels, and lay in No Man's Land for 48 hours.

'You were very near to death,' I said to him when we were married. 'Did you see angels or hear voices, or even feel you were being prepared for

99

Glamour personified, plus personality and universal originality.

'I can only say I personally never think about getting older because I am not getting older.

Every morning I swim about one hour if I am not at the Studio – then I work about 2–3 hours with my secretaries. I go horseback riding whenever I can and in Palm Beach at my vacation house I play Polo every morning on my gorgeous horse "Whiplash". I fence, play ice-hockey and have a prize-winning Tennessee Walking Horse called "Summer Delight". I ride her and show her all the time.

I don't like to go to bed late (I love parties, but I am always the first to leave) as I get up around 6.00 every morning.

I love the mornings – that's when I feed my five dogs – 3 Shih Tzus and 2 German Shepherds. I cut up turkey and chicken for them and spoil the life out of them.

I have a twenty-six year old daughter, and since I am twenty-one we passed our age somewhere along the road!

I love gorgeous animals, gorgeous clothes, gorgeous jewellery, gorgeous men, gorgeous women and gorgeous everything.

I drink almost nothing and do not smoke. Also I do not eat red meat if I can help it, and love fruits and vegetables the most.

By the way, I don't believe in a face lift unless it is really necessary. I never had one – thank God for my Hungarian bone structure. On many ladies a face lift can make them look older than they are. After all, what is wrong with some wrinkles? I think they are sexy and exciting on men and women. It shows they had a past.'

another world?'

'No,' he replied, 'I just felt very tired and far away from all the noise of the battle.'

The second night, Hugh was carried in on a man's back and received a number of shrapnel wounds in the process. In the Field Dressing Station they treated only the shrapnel wounds, not realizing he was injured elsewhere.

When he eventually arrived at a Red Cross Hospital in Calais he was so covered in mud through being dropped by his stretcher bearers who were afraid of the continual shelling they did not realize he was an Officer.

By that time he was so ill that the doctors decided there was no chance of his surviving and, as was the practice in those days, put him outside the hospital in a tent to die.

His parents crossed the Channel to see him for the last time. Because he had been taken to a rich hospital run by the Canadians, they got him over the shock by just dressing his wounds and giving him port and champagne as they did so, while the rest of the time he was under heroin.

It was only at almost the end of the last War that we learnt that a terribly injured patient should be left untouched to get over the shock. It was what saved my husband's life in 1918.

After attending five hospitals and having innumerable operations he was told when he was discharged: 'It is a miracle you are alive. Nothing more can be done by surgery. Never let anyone fiddle about with you. You must trust to nature and live with your disability.'

He did suffer from terrible bronchitis when I married him in 1936, however, and he would cough all night until a piece of bone or part of the shell which had injured him worked its way out of his body.

I cured his bronchitis by giving him comb honey night and morning, and despite everything the doctors had said, we had such a long, happy and perfect marriage that I remember no problems whatever.

In 1963, one day after we had celebrated 27 years together, he collapsed when the scar tissue from the terrible wounds he had received 45 years earlier finally affected his heart.

It was a wonderful death as far as he was concerned, but a terrible shock for me, and I kept thinking that I had not only lost him, but that he did not believe there was any 'after-life'.

We had talked about it often and he always said: 'I have been nearer to death than almost anybody else, and I had no feeling there was any other world then, so why should I think it now? When one is dead, one is dead!'

Then something very strange happened. A week after his funeral my maid who had been with me for over 25 years, said: 'Have you noticed the wonderful smell of carnations outside your bedroom?'

I thought it was strange because there had been no carnations in the house since the funeral, and as it had taken place in December, the wreaths had no fragrance.

At that time my second son Glen was living with me and I used to get up early each morning to give him his breakfast before he went to London.

When I went out of my bedroom I was suddenly aware of a marvellous, almost overpowering scent of carnations. They were unlike any carnations I had ever smelt in England. It was the exotic fragrance of Malmaison, which I had not seen for years.

I stood for a moment feeling astounded, then hurried downstairs in case my son missed his train. When he had gone I returned upstairs and the scent was still there, but fainter. I thought I must have imagined it, but the following morning it was there again.

It came, I discovered, in patches. Some mornings it wasn't there and I couldn't smell it until I returned upstairs after breakfast.

The fragrance came and went for over a month and I knew exactly why.

My husband had always bought me red carnations when we went to Paris for our 'second honeymoons'. The first thing we would do was to drive to the Madeleine where we went into the church and said a prayer at the Chapel of St Joseph and the Virgin Mary for our marriage. Outside there were always rows of colourful flowerstalls and every year my husband bought me a huge bunch of red carnations and I arranged them in our bedroom. Each evening before we went out to dinner he would put one in his buttonhole.

If there was anything that was a symbol of our happiness and our closeness to each other, it was red carnations. That was how I understood why the scent of them was outside my door.

It could only mean one thing – he was trying to tell me that I had been right. He was proving that there is an 'after-life'. There *is* survival after death.

MADAME DE POMPADOUR

Exquisite, beautiful, she was, despite
King Louis XV's adoring love for her,
a cold woman.

She tried to make herself passionate by
eating oysters, celery and truffles but they
only made her ill.

In the end she realized that Nature's
charm and the adoration she gave the
King could keep him at her feet more
effectively than anything else.

Having dealt fully with the mind and the spirit, I think we should now look at what there is to help us to keep the actual body young or make it younger.

From a woman's point of view, the first thing of really vital importance is that when she is over 40 she should begin to think about taking estrogen. Women can, I think, remain looking feminine and feeling full of vitality for ever if they take estrogen under medical supervision.

When I was 40 estrogen was comparatively unknown in Britain, although America was just beginning to be aware of it.

It was not until I was 60 that I learnt of the three marvellous natural estrogenic hormone preparations that prevent the 'change of life' and all the symptoms of it. (In the UK they are marketed under the names Premarin, Harmogen and Progynova.)

Now 90 per cent of American women use them on prescription, which means they do not suffer from hot flushes, nightsweat and menopausal depression, nor – and this is very important – the drying up or shrinking of the vagina, which in some women can make intercourse very painful.

I first learnt about this from a book called *Forever Feminine* by Dr Robert Wilson, consultant in gynaecology at three famous American hospitals.

When I talked about it in England nobody seemed to know what I was saying until a book called *No Change* by Wendy Cooper caught the public imagination.

She and I appeared on numerous programmes, and gradually women were alerted to what they had been deprived of for so long.

I take conjugated estrogens (in the form of Premarin) and at 82 I would not be without them for anything in the world. They keep me young and keep me feeling warm and loving.

Estrogen also prevents brittle bones in older women (although there are other treatments). A world expert on osteoporosis says that a fracture has never been seen once therapy has been properly instituted. In layman's terms, what it does is to 'keep the juice in the bones'. After my mother fractured a bone in her leg when she was 96 the doctors gave it to her, I thought a little late, so that she was less likely to fracture another one.

Following a hysterectomy HRT (Hormone Replacement Therapy) is essential, because it keeps a woman unwithered inside, prevents wrinkles and all the irritation, nerves and frustrations of approaching age.

At first people told me I was talking nonsense and that the change of life was natural.

It is no more natural than refusing to have your teeth stopped if they decay, or wearing glasses. No woman should suffer unnecessarily for what inevitably happens between 40 and 50, and she need suffer from none of the usual effects if she takes estrogen.

Recently Dr Peter Layde – Director of the US Center for Disease Control in Atlanta, Georgia announced that women who use the contraceptive pill are less likely to develop cancer of the womb or ovaries than those who do not. As the contraceptive pill contains estrogen and progesterone, this is exactly what I have been advocating in Hormone Replacement Therapy.

Dr Robert Wilson in his book, which converted me, said that after experimenting with over 5,000 patients he found those who were given estrogen during the menopause looked and felt younger. He also said the shortage of estrogen which occurred at that time, produced various symptoms, including a vulnerability to illness and ageing.

Hormone Replacement Therapy is therefore extremely important for women who wish to remain young.

From my own experience, it makes so much difference that I find it infuriating when women write to me to say that their doctors will not prescribe it because they think it is unnecessary.

To quote Dr Wilson again, he wrote: 'If a man withered *outside* as a woman withers *inside* at this time, he would very quickly do something about it!'

Most modern doctors are, however, much more amenable and there are now Hormone Replacement Clinics at almost every major hospital in England.

But of course there are always the people who are ready to 'shoot down' anything new, and some doctors have suggested that too much estrogen may cause cancer, and a great number of women are worried about it.

From my long experience I am convinced they are wrong and that they have been confusing those who could have benefited from estrogen.

Now we learn from Dr Peter Layde that the two cancers which annually kill more than 4,000 women in Britain are in fact twice as common amongst those who do not take the pill as those who have taken it.

The authors of this study, which involved 3,200 women at eight different American centers, say that this particular effect of the pill could, if confirmed, have a very large public health impact by saving lives.

Estrogen also prevents the acceleration of the aches, pains and diseases to which we are all prone, and which accelerates during the menopause.

For those who have been frightened by their doctors about estrogen, let me tell you that I have now taken HRT for nearly 20 years, and will continue to go on taking it until I die. It has now been proved that Evening Primrose Oil, Efamol is very effective in all menstrual troubles. It can be bought in the UK and the USA.

Having started off with the women who at the change of life reach the old age of youth and the youth of old age, we must think about the men.

My husband, having had such a long medical history behind him, was determined to interfere as little with nature as possible. He fought against taking vitamins after I had become so enthusiastic about them in the early Fifties.

A great many men feel the same, so I invented for them a very special capsule which contains three essential vitamins for those who are not as young as they used to be.

'I will take one tablet!' my husband used to say. So I devised one which is of immense benefit to all the other husbands who say the same thing and run for the train to the office. This special capsule is called *GEB6, and it contains Ginseng, Vitamin E and Vitamin B_6 which is specially beneficial to nerves.

I had never heard of Ginseng until I was in Hong Kong in 1968 and I was standing with a Chinese stockbroker looking down at the fantastic panorama of the harbour with its liners, battleships, junks and masses of small sampans.

We were talking about Chinese medicine and he said to me: 'Every one of the people in the sampans saves up to buy Ginseng. They take it with brandy.'

I had no idea what Ginseng was, and it was only later that I found out Ginseng was first written about in China in the 1st century BC. It is also mentioned in the ancient *Atharva Veda*.

In 1714 Father Jartoux, a missionary for many years amongst the Chinese, wrote a whole book on Ginseng. The Chinese consider it the supreme remedy for any sort of sexual inadequacy, and the finest grades of Chinese Ginseng have long been reputed to have the power to restore fertility, even to those who have passed the normal child-bearing age.

The Ancient Greeks spoke of Ginseng as an important ingredient in love philtres, but in China Ginseng was so precious that only the Emperor was allowed to take it.

But all this knowledge was kept in the East.

When my old friend in Hong Kong told me about it I discovered that Ginseng was very expensive. In fact, in 1968 it was £50 a pound! And although he gave me some, I thought it very unlikely that many people in England would be able to afford it.

I came home and talked to scientists in the health business, and now Ginseng is available very cheaply in every Healthfood Store.

First Lady of the American Theatre. Has received 40 Honorary Degrees. A Broadway theatre was named for her and on the Opening Night she was awarded the Gold Medal of the City of New York.

'My words of wisdom would be most unworthy anyway for I have never made any conscious move to keep young and active. I have simply forged ahead doing what comes naturally. My chief weapon against stultifying with age has been a keen interest in everything under the sun. I was born with that.

I have never abused my physical being with drinking or smoking or bad diet. Since I have been a performer from the age of eight, I had to keep in training for that. I used to walk two to three miles a day, but have slowed up on that in my eighties. That's all the golden wisdom I have to impart.'

When the last astronauts went from America to the moon, they were given it as a compulsory part of their diet.

I find Ginseng so wonderful that it is difficult to think how we used to manage without it. It prevents jet lag completely, and I gave some to our Prime Minister, Mrs Thatcher, after she confessed that on very long journeys she sometimes suffered in that way.

Ginseng sharpens the brain, and this is borne out by a Chinese contention for generations that it is important for all circulatory diseases. The Chinese have also discovered that in many cases where people have been practically dead, when given a good quality Ginseng root they have been sufficiently revitalized to carry on their business.

There is a great deal of proof, far more than I can say here, that Ginseng will combat impotence and the onset of senility. Travellers in China from Marco Polo onwards have been extremely impressed with the ability of Chinese men of advanced years – and the Chinese themselves readily admit it is the use of Ginseng which is responsible.

As I have already told you, the Russians are enthusiastic about Ginseng. I know that I could not possibly do without it.

At the moment I am taking Indian Ginseng, which I find very good and very invigorating. No one seems to know that the natives of India have been using their Ginseng, called 'Ashwagandha', for thousands of years, and it has as much folklore attached to it as the Korean and Siberian varieties. Punarvasu Atreya, who was a university teacher of medicine in the Punjab in 1,000 BC, described the numerous uses of Ashwagandha in female disorders.

Bhavaprakakasha, who lived later, mentioned that Ashwagandha 'improved body strength as a bitter tonic and astringent: it is also known to stimulate sex impulses and improve sperms'.

Older people in India use Ashwagandha to relieve limb tremors, for rejuvenation, or as an aphrodisiac.

It seems extraordinary now that we have so much Ginseng available that this marvellous man-shaped root of the Orient has been kept a secret for over 5,000 years. Now it is very much with us, and I know of nothing better than Ginseng to overcome exhaustion and to stimulate the body both sexually and mentally.

The next ingredient in my special capsule is Vitamin E. It seems unnecessary to tell you that it is essential for human blood, improves the circulation and makes oxygen available for every muscle and tissue in our bodies.

Vitamin E was one of the first vitamins in which I was really interested in 1935. My brother at that time was the first Tory MP to go down to the Distressed Areas. He visited Aneurin Bevan's constituency in Ebbw Vale and saw a man dying in the street from starvation.

The horrors of unemployment in those days were very different from what they are now, although I still believe that unemployment is degrading and something no human being should be asked to endure.

But the suffering in what was known as the Distressed Areas, especially in Wales and the North of England, was terrifying in the Thirties.

I was so horrified at what my brother told me he had seen that I began to work with Lady Rhys-Williams – whose son, the Member of Parliament for South Kensington is now in the European Parliament – in giving women Vitamin B to prevent them from having habitual miscarriages and from malnutrition.

I was so impressed at the results, although what everybody in the Distressed Areas really needed was food, that I began to study vitamins and found that Vitamin E in those days was only given to pregnant mares.

It was not until after World War II that it was found to be an essential element in preventing miscarriages.

Vitamin E also helps children to grow, relieves varicose veins in old legs, which I have proved over and over again, and taken both internally and when applied to the skin can erase scars.

Linda Clarke, one of America's most widely read health advisors, believes that Vitamin E is essential to male virility – which I have always known myself.

Lots of people come to me and ask: 'How can we have a baby? The doctors say there is no reason why we should not have one, but nothing happens!'

I reply that they will have one if they both take my vitamins, and I give them a list: the most important one is Vitamin E.

One wife had her first baby after being married 12 years and now has four children.

Vitamin E is essential for treating any form of heart trouble, as I have already said, and it helps victims of a stroke to regain the movements of their limbs and mental functions.

An Italian doctor made the first findings concerning Vitamin E in relation to diabetes. Last year a friend told me his wife was taking more and more insulin and he was worried about it. I suggested that she should take Vitamin E. After three days she was feeling much better, and the doctor decided she needed less insulin.

But what we are concerned with in this book is that Vitamin E is used for stress in old age.

Extensive research done at the University of Montreal by Professor Hans Segal has found that Vitamin E almost completely inhibits heart disease, makes the kidneys normal, and helps prevent the symptoms of ageing.

Now you will understand why I included Vitamin E in my capsule which, to make it easier, I call the 'Stress Pill'.

The last and most important ingredient is Vitamin B$_6$.

For many years it was assumed that we get all the B$_6$ we need in our diets. It has now been established that many people can be deficient in this very important vitamin.

A recent study by Adele Davis has shown that hospital patients given a diet adequate except for Vitamin B$_6$ may develop mental depression, sore mouths, lips and tongues, insomnia, extreme weakness, nervousness, giddiness, nausea and vomiting. The most strange reaction, however, is eczema which appears first on the scalp and the eyebrows, round the nose and behind the ears.

When B$_6$ is given to these patients, their condition quickly becomes normal.

Doctors now say, somewhat belatedly, that any woman on the pill should be given B$_6$. They have discovered that tantrums in some children may be partly inspired by a B$_6$ deficiency, and as I have said for a long time, Vitamin B$_6$ is the answer to what many people call 'my nerves'.

It was also discovered a year or so ago that Vitamin B$_6$ completely stops pregnancy sickness.

A friend of mine whose daughter was married to a Peer who was desperately anxious to have an heir, rang me up to say that she was feeling so sick during her pregnancy that she did not think she could go through with it.

'Even if she drinks water,' my friend said, 'she is sick. What can we do?'

I gave her B$_6$ and within 24 hours the sickness vanished never to return.

But more important than anything else, B$_6$ is the answer to those who feel they must have a sedative or a tranquillizer and they are given it by their doctors without thinking of the inevitable side-effects.

I have found that my Stress Pill, GEB6, is not only a best-seller in the Health Movement, but that many people are much better in themselves, full of new ideas which they can tackle with a new energy.

This is exactly what is wanted in Britain today, and so I feel this most successful formula is a contribution in a very important way to the future of the country, as well as to ourselves.

MUMTAZ MAHAL

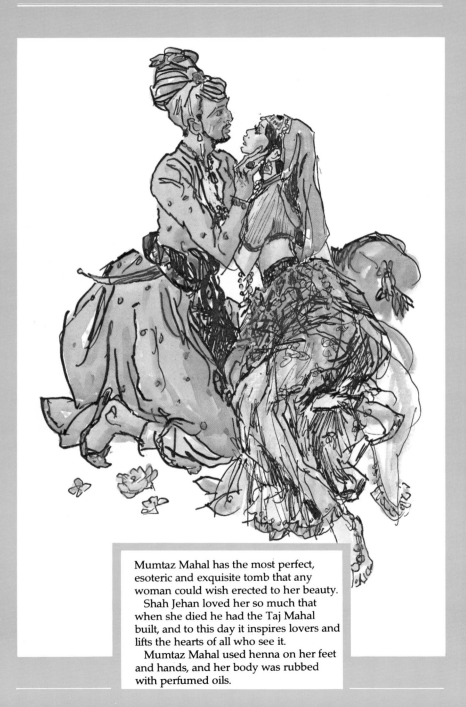

Mumtaz Mahal has the most perfect,
esoteric and exquisite tomb that any
woman could wish erected to her beauty.

Shah Jehan loved her so much that
when she died he had the Taj Mahal
built, and to this day it inspires lovers and
lifts the hearts of all who see it.

Mumtaz Mahal used henna on her feet
and hands, and her body was rubbed
with perfumed oils.

The question that comes to everyone when they get to old age is whether they can continue making love.

As I have said previously, this should go on indefinitely, until you actually die. And for goodness sake, never say or think you are too old.

Clark Gable who reigned as King of Hollywood for more than 30 years and of whom it was known that every woman he ever met was in love with him, always said: 'I prefer older women – they have seen more, heard more, and know more than a demure young girl . . . I'll take an older woman every time!'

Victor Hugo, who was larger than life in literature and in love, is estimated to have had sex with at least 200 women between 1820 and 1848.

At the age of 70 he seduced the 22-year-old daughter of Théophile Gautier (another writer) and was at the same time known to be having a relationship with Sarah Bernhardt.

Madame de Maintenon was 48 when she secretly married Louis XIV of France, who had all the lustful sensuality of the Bourbons. When she was 70 she wrote to the Bishop asking if she must continue to make love every day with the King as it made her so tired. The Bishop replied she must submit to her husband's wishes. She therefore shared the King's bed until she was 81 when he died.

La Bella Otero was one of the great courtesans of all time. Her beautiful breasts are supposed to have been copied on the towers of the Carlton Hotel at Cannes. Unlike many of her contemporaries she actually enjoyed sex, and said when she died at 97: 'I have been a slave to my passions but never to a man!'

She was fascinated, on her 40th birthday, by Aristide Briand — later to be France's greatest statesman and winner of the 1926 Nobel Peace Prize. He was 50 at the time, and Otero recalled: 'Once . . . he made love to me eight times before morning.'

Their affair lasted for 10 years.

H. G. Wells was another lover who was not frustrated by old age. I met him in 1922 and young though I was at the time, I realized it would be dangerous to be alone with him. He was, in fact, just ending an affair with Rebecca West, one of Britain's foremost journalists and novelists. It had started in 1912 and lasted for 10 years.

Wells then fell for a former nun, a Dutch woman. Having written to each other, they met in Geneva where she received him in her bedroom in the dark and led him straight to her bed.

Until his death in 1946 Wells was never without a woman, and was sexually active until almost the end of his 80 years.

Mark Twain, America's most brilliant writer, was not a very amorous man himself but he wrote a great deal about sex. He calculated that a man was good for 100 acts of love a year for 50 years – while a woman was good for 3,000 a year, an average of 10 a day, for as long as she lived.

I think this is nonsense, although undoubtedly the question often arises when a man is afraid of failing and therefore abstains.

To 'make love' competently, it is very important that it should be continuous and without long intervals between the moments of loving. When we 'make love', we use every muscle in our bodies. It is therefore excellent for our health, and any doctor who says you should abstain is talking nonsense.

'Making love' keeps one young, active, energetic and of course, happy.

Naturally, as the years go by, love-making is not as frequent as it was when one was young and it was a spontaneous daily action. But the fact that it does happen is the best and most wonderful tonic that could ever be prescribed for a man or a woman.

Desire is a strange thing and no one yet has produced a comprehensive book or thesis on what causes desire in human beings or why everyone in some small particular is different.

What is important in a marriage is to remember that when one's partner desires love, it is not something to be put off and set on one side until later.

It is the English, of course, who have almost made it a rule that love-making should take place at night when one is tired and if possible in the dark.

Latin nations are much more sensible, and I have always believed that the best time for love-making is immediately after luncheon, when in foreign countries they have a siesta.

Men, however, often find that they feel more eager for love first thing in the morning, and a wise wife who loves her husband will never refuse, whatever the time may be.

Nor should she ever despair of attracting her husband if sometimes he fails her.

The fabulous film star Rudolph Valentino, who was 'passion personified' in *The Sheik*, was divorced by his first wife because their marriage was never consummated. But with his second wife he said: 'She made me touch ecstasy!'

Later Pola Negri wrote in her autobiography: 'Valentino's true sexuality reached out and captured me.' He took her, she says, in a perfect act of love.

Voltaire, the brilliant, witty, French satirist, said at 46 he was 'too old to make love'. Yet at 51 he was having a passionate affair with his pretty, witty niece which lasted until his death. And at 79 he tried so hard to seduce a very attractive young woman that he fainted three times!

There are fortunately, in the Health Movement, things to help older people who may feel nervous that their love-making is not as competent as it used to be and think they need a slight stimulus from natural herbs.

There is something new which has just become very popular called Muira Puama. It is not very well known in the West, but it has been used by Brazilians since time immemorial, and is reported in Brazil to be one of the most powerful aphrodisiacs available.

Do not be worried by the word 'aphrodisiac' because every food, herb, root, shrub, leaf and tree has at some time been known as an aphrodisiac.

Tomatoes for instance were, in the reign of Charles II, known as 'love apples'. The Puritans banned them as dangerous and actually put about the story that they were poisonous to prevent people from eating them.

We are all aware that oysters, truffles and mushrooms have a long history as aphrodisiacs.

But so have fish and meat, and the Ancient Greeks frequently mentioned onions as stimulating sexual desire.

Mushrooms were a sacred food used to create trances and hallucinations, but were also known to the Greeks as the aphrodisiac food of the gods.

The Romans put great faith in meat and fish. Horace, writing to enquire about a seaside resort (*Epistles* 1:15), wanted to know if he could count on a supply of 'the meat of hares, wild boars, fish and sea urchins'. He hoped to become young again and win the favour of women.

Ovid, in *The Art of Love*, advised aspiring lovers to take a diet of white onions, eggs, green vegetables, honey and the nuts of the pine tree.

Pliny advised river snails preserved in salt and taken with wine, sparrows or the eggs of sparrows, the tongue of a goose, leeks, and the yolks of five pigeons' eggs in honey with a bit of hog's lard.

Both Pliny and Athenaeus mention the carrot as an aphrodisiac.

The *Kama Sutra* advises boiling asparagus and treacle in cow's milk and ghee, to be eaten once a day to increase sexual power and prolong life.

The Indians also believed in rice and sparrow eggs to be cooked in milk to produce a thick custard and then mixed with honey and ghee.

The *Ananga-Ranga* advocates seeds of the herb mungo soaked in milk and sugar, dried for three days in the sun, then ground to a powder. This should then be kneaded into a cake and fried in ghee, to be eaten every morning.

Long before America discovered the breakfast food and advertised it as an

The most alluring, sophisticated gentleman of the screen. Cary Grant's brilliant success lies in the fact that he plays himself. He has the looks, the talent and the maniacal drive to work and an irresistible personal appeal which increases rather than fades as he grows older.

'Well now, if you didn't cleverly select to be born of long-lived parents, as I did, then the first requisite for lengthening your life span is, of course, just to keep breathing in and out, or vice versa, and while continuing that necessary action, permit me to suggest that, providing you feel up to a little light exercise, you swim. Swim whenever, or wherever, possible. It's a pleasant soothing sensation. You don't have to be an expert. Any stroke at all. Your entire body is subjected to the water's equal pressure all around you, after learning to breathe rhythmically and relaxed while swimming, you will find no better or easier way of conditioning yourself. A swimmer's figure, whether his or her frame is long or short, slim or stocky is, you'll note, always well-proportioned. However, if it's not possible for you to swim regularly, then the next best exercise is walking. As much as you can. As often as you can; striding along while, yet again, breathing rhythmically and relaxed.

However the most effective exercise calculated to add years to your life, but very difficult to do, is pushing away from the dinner table!'

energizer for growing children, India had a breakfast food very like a cereal to invigorate the elderly.

In *The Perfumed Garden*, which is undoubtedly an extremely pornographic book, Sheikh Nefzaoui recommended the yolks of eggs with onions, green peas, powdered with ginger, cinnamon, and cardamom, also camel's milk and honey. For quick results the Sheikh advocated eggs fried in fresh butter and fat worked into a mass of honey and eaten with a little bread.

It would be a desperate lover who would tackle this!

In the Middle Ages the Mediterranean world combined to offer the rest of Europe a wide selection of aphrodisiac foods.

The physician Paul of Aegina assured his patients that sea foods made excellent aphrodisiacs, especially the octopus. Next in importance he advised snails, mussels, clams and oysters, and for vegetables he thought well of turnips, chick-peas, kidney beans and peppers. Grapes, which were said to promote desire by supplying the body with moisture and the blood with air, would make an appropriate dessert.

Later, in the reign of Louis XIV, the French thought grapes very important to a feast which ended in a great deal of love-making.

I could continue quoting to you almost every sort of food you have ever eaten yourself or heard about, but of course the best aphrodisiac is to be strong, healthy, and to be with somebody attractive of the opposite sex.

To return however to Muira Puama, this product from Brazil is perfectly safe with no side-effects, and although it is suggested that one should take two or three capsules a day, it would not hurt to take more. It is sold in the UK and USA.

Muira Puama is in a new health product (sold under the brand-name Libidex 5) with ingredients which you already know are tremendously important in stimulating extra energy and mental appreciation. These are Siberian Ginseng, Vitamin E, Zinc and Selenium.

When you take any virility pill for the first time I suggest you also take two or three vitamin B_6; this will prevent you from feeling tense, which is always restrictive in regard to sex.

The second product that I recommend and have known for many years is *Keitafo Banlon, which is a Chinese tonic with Ginseng, gives one a special zest, and definitely arouses the desire for love in those who take it.

It contains a great many herbs that are known only to the Chinese, who are past masters in this sort of medicine. I have discussed the contents with the wife of the Chinese doctor — he does not speak English — who makes it in Hong Kong, and she assures me that only the very best fresh herbs were used in the product.

*only available in Britain

I have tried it myself for many years and given it to a great number of people, and I know how excellent it is.

To return to desire, it is important for us all to realize that some people have different ideas and fantasies where desire is concerned.

I always remember when I was very young and had just written my first novel which came out in 1923, an older woman saying to me: 'As you are a novelist, I want to ask you something very personal.'

She told me that her husband, when he made love to her, always wished her to wear long kid gloves because it reminded him of their wedding day.

In those days when no one talked of sex and it was not written about as it is now, I had never heard of any fantasies with regard to love-making. But I was sensible enough to reply: 'Of course if that is what he wants, you must please him, and perhaps give him a treat with coloured ones.'

I am always glad now that I was not shocked nor even appeared surprised at what she told me.

Unless a man wants something sadistic, really unpleasant, or crude pornography, it is sensible if one loves him very much and wants to make him happy, to play along with his ideas and enjoy them too.

Love-making is, especially for a man, a sensitive action and he can so easily be upset or humiliated if he is not appreciated.

As I have said elsewhere in this book, a wise woman will always tell a man he is a wonderful lover, and hope he will become one!

For tired or sore eyes take Vitamin B2. In winter a Vitamin C tablet (1000 mg) every day will help to prevent colds.

12

There are two 'give-aways', I am always told, which reveal one's age far more effectively than anything else. One is our hands, because it is almost impossible to disguise ageing hands with cosmetics, and the other is our voice.

Voices are tremendously important at any time, which is something we often forget.

Sarah Bernhardt's 'Golden Voice' combined with her beauty, unique talent and overwhelming personality, made her worshipped in France, and adored in America and England.

But her will-power and her courage were remarkable.

In 1915 after war had broken out the previous year, she was 71. She had been very ill and had a leg amputated, yet she insisted on going to the front to entertain the French troops. The authorities were aghast at the idea, but she persisted, and they sent a young actor to accompany her.

He wrote: 'Beneath the painted and tinselled decrepitude of the old actress there lies an inextinguishable sun.'

The journey was exhausting. Sarah, carried on a litter-chair, was motored over rutted roads, half shattered by bombs. The first performance was in an open market-place where a crude stage with makeshift footlights and a flimsy curtain had been erected. Over 2,000 soldiers sat on benches or squatted on the ground, many of them wounded.

The announcement that they were to see Madame Sarah Bernhardt was received in dead silence.

The curtain flitted back to reveal a fragile, wispy old woman propped up against pillows in a shabby armchair. She began to speak the patriotic piece she had selected.

Someone present wrote: 'A miracle took place. Sarah, old, mutilated, once more illuminated a crowd by the rays of her genius. This fragile creature, ill, wounded and immobile could still, through the magic of her spoken word, re-instill heroism into those soldiers weary from battle.'

When she finished with the clarion call of *Aux armes* 2,000 men rose to their feet cheering, some of them weeping.

The ancient Egyptian priests used their voices to conjure up fire and also, we have always believed, to destroy.

Many years ago the son of a very important businessman was found dead in his rooms at Oxford. There was apparently no reason at all for his death, but on the table in front of him was a book in the Ancient Egyptian language open at the word for death. What was assumed at the time was that he had found the right pronunciation of the word, which of course no one knows, and had killed himself in doing so.

But voices, as we all know, can charm and beguile, and also irritate and anger.

I often find that I am repelled by the way people speak on the telephone, and I tell my secretaries always to be very careful, as they are speaking for me, not to give offence.

For example, I find it insulting when I ring up and ask: 'Can I speak to Mrs X please?'

'She's out!'

'When will she be back?'

'No idea. Ring back later!'

The telephone is slammed down – and that makes me feel so cross not with the speaker, but with Mrs X herself because she employs such an unpleasant person.

I am absolutely certain that people, especially women who speak with quiet, gentle voices, get far more attention from men, and get their own way far easier than women who are sharp and aggressive.

My second son, who is very critical, says that half the troubles in the world now are due to women having aggressive, hard voices, and I think sometimes he has a point.

It is, however, very easy for men and women as they get old to talk in a hoarse, geriatric manner which I find very depressing.

The reason for this is that they breathe in the wrong way.

One of the most famous Yogi writers says: 'Only by conscious regulation of our breathing can we achieve the resistance which assures us a long life free of sickness.'

This is such an important statement that it must make us wonder whether because we breathe by instinct we do not think enough about what is actually the most important thing to keep us alive.

A great friend of mine who was taught to breathe by Sarah Bernhardt used to say: 'Do learn about your body, why it breathes, what happens when it does. People learn how their cars work, but they are quite uninterested in the most marvellous machine in the world.'

She was quite right – most people know nothing about their breathing except that they do.

When I had a very serious operation and was feeling ghastly after it, a special breathing expert came to teach me, she said, to breathe.

Ill though I was, I was delighted to surprise her by showing that I could breathe properly in the Yoga fashion.

It is very easy to learn to breathe properly, and once you have mastered it you do it automatically.

As you breathe in your ribs must move out horizontally, and the breast bone come forward. This means that the capacity of the lungs is increased on both sides and at the front. When the inhalation is completed, the diaphragm moves upwards and the breast bone moves to the rear, the lungs are squeezed together as the air is expelled from them.

With really deep, rhythmic breathing other muscles are brought into play.

Far too many people get only the slightest movement in the ribs and very little in the diaphragm so that they are always depriving themselves of oxygen.

Correct breathing not only vitalizes the whole body, as I have said, with life-giving oxygen, but it is the most certain way to improve your skin.

Once you are breathing properly you will find your voice deepens and becomes more resonant, and this is when, if you are sensible, you will practise breathing in the Yoga manner.

In 1978 when I sang my *Album of Love Songs* with the Royal Philharmonic Orchestra, I had not sung for 40 years, and it was naturally a tremendous effort to get my voice back. I was then 77 and I think the oldest person ever to have made her first album at that age.

I took great care to breathe deeply, and when I had a moment to myself I did the real Yoga breathing.

This is quite simple. You can either sit upright or do it lying flat in bed.

You draw in your breath while you silently count eight, hold it while you count sixteen, and let it out equally slowly while you count eight.

It is extraordinary what a difference this can make to your voice in a very short time, and is what the monks in the Tibetan monasteries do when they intone the wonderful words: *'Om Mani Padme Hum.'* which means: 'Hail to the Jewel on the Lotus.'

In order to develop the low, deep note which is almost like the buzzing of a bee, they have a special exercise, which I also did, in the open air. I could feel my voice responding.

1. Inhale a complete breath very slowly and steadily through the nostrils, taking as much time as possible on the inhalation.
2. Retain for 16 seconds.
3. Expel air vigorously in one great breath with your mouth opened as wide as possible.

'Of course the obvious things *are* obvious! Diet – Exercise – Sleep – Relaxation – all of these are essential. But I think the most important effort one must make is a mental one.

It is vital to be positive and not negative in the onslaught of the years! But! If every time you say: "Oh! I am so tired," "Oh! My bones are creaking," "Oh! I am too *old* for that!"

If every time you say these phrases, or think them, if you deny their power over you, and answer: "NO! I am not tired," "NO! My bones are not creaking," "NO! I am NEVER going to be 'too old'," your spirits are lifted and you are ready to face ANYTHING!

I know it sounds simplistic! But just TRY it! As an actress I have many times felt I could not drag myself to the theatre one more time.

But when it comes, I am like a race-horse, snorting and tossing my head and waiting impatiently for the gates to open – in my case, the curtain to go up!

I *do* realize that I am blessed with having a profession . . . one that *demands* energy and youth, even if you are eighty years old!

What it comes down to is "MIND OVER MATTER", and I cannot recommend this medicine too highly!'

Sensitive, unfailing good taste, memorable on and off the screen.

You will find this affects the vocal organs and also helps your facial muscles. Try this experiment:

Stand before a mirror, pucker up your mouth and whistle. See the shape of your mouth and the general expression of your face. Then sing or speak as you do naturally, and see the difference.

Start to whistle again for a few seconds, then without changing the position of your lips or face, sing a few notes. You will notice a new vibrant, resonant, clear and beautiful tone is produced.

There are many other breathing exercises that the Yogis do to stimulate the lungs and produce their voices, but you will find this quite simple and very, very effective.

Yoga, which many people just look on as something fanciful and Oriental, is used by a great number of actors and actresses.

Evelyn Laye told me years ago that she had learned to relax in Yoga fashion, and always does it before she goes on the stage so she will give a really good performance because she is not feeling 'on edge' or tense in any way.

Mrs Indira Gandhi, of course, knows the true value of Yoga, and all the great Indian leaders like her father Pandit Nehru have availed themselves of the practical as well as the mystical side of the Indian religions.

Yehudi Menuhin, the world famous violinist, tells a delightful story of when he had first started to practise Yoga.

He visited India and on his first night in Delhi was challenged by Pandit Nehru to show what he could do. 'I stood on my head in a somewhat rickety and unsatisfactory fashion,' he says. ' "Oh, that is no good!" said Nehru in his sharp way, "I'll show you." He took off his little Gandhi hat and very elegantly . . . up-ended himself on the drawing-room carpet.'

Yehudi goes on in his biography to say that for him Yoga is primarily an inner peace which he finds as soon as he breathes deeply and evenly. Yoga also influenced and directed his marvellous playing and India itself opened for him new horizons. As he says himself: 'Every experience pushed me further – a passage to India – and of course, specifically Yoga taught me lessons it would have taken years to elaborate for myself.'

David Ben-Gurion, Israel's first Prime Minister, who has been called an 'Israeli Abraham Lincoln', was the second statesman for whom Yehudi Menuhin stood on his head, for he also practised Yoga.

But to return to the voice: so many women pitch their voices too high when they are young and when they are old let it drop too low.

Try to keep a lilt in your voice which makes people feel that you are happy and gives them an answering feeling of happiness.

One of the greatest compliments I can be paid after I have talked to somebody on the telephone, is for them to say: 'You are like a tonic. I really feel better after talking to you!'

That is what you can do with your voice. It is not always what we say, but the way we talk.

Of course we all know that women with soft, hesitating, childlike voices are irresistible to strong men who wish to protect them.

Marilyn Monroe had this sort of voice and every man who met her fell for it. Jackie Onassis is another person who has a soft, feminine voice, and I make many of my heroines talk like them because I know how effective it is.

My brother Ronald, as I have mentioned was the first Member of Parliament to be killed in the war. At 33 he was known as a visionary and an idealist so that many people were certain he would be a future Prime Minister.

He was a compelling speaker because he used the power in which we both believed, which came from his solar plexus. This is really where we breathe and give out what I call magnetism, and what the Yogis call *Prana*.

Prana is behind all thought and all energy, and it is something which pours from us when we speak or when we express any emotion.

The Greeks believed this and on their drawings they made the rays of light or 'power' come from the solar plexus.

But then the Christians, for some reason of their own, took this manifestation of the 'Life Force', put it on the heads of their saints and called it a 'halo'.

If you feel deeply about anything, you use this force from your solar plexus, which is why if you have ever spoken in public at any time, you will often feel tired as you sit down because you have given so much of yourself.

This is the magnetism, and I might also say the magic of all great orators, all great leaders, and all people who influence or teach us.

I must have been about 20 when I first heard David Lloyd George – Prime Minister of the UK during the First World War – speak, and although I cannot remember what he said, I can still remember the vital vibrations that came from him and the manner in which everybody sat in silence, spellbound until he had finished speaking.

It is a power which can make or break a leader, whether he or she is political, religious or merely self-seeking. But whatever leaders are doing it for, it comes from their solar plexus to their voice.

Nowadays, with radio and television, we hear voices all the time, and it always seems to me extraordinary that so many of the voices who are chosen by the 'powers that be' to speak to us either have voices that are unpleasant, difficult to hear, or else sound unnatural over the air.

But there is no doubt that one can change one's voice, and this has been proved very ably by Mrs Thatcher. When she first became Prime Minister her voice was not very effective and often sounded somewhat superficial. Now she speaks in a soft, sincere, gentle manner which is the admiration of everyone who understands Elocution, and also undoubtedly charms her audience.

If she can change her voice, so can you.

Take the trouble to find out how your voice sounds by recording it on tape. This can be done quite easily and you will be surprised how different your voice sounds from what you imagined it would be.

I was horrified the other day when from America I received a recording of a television interview to find out how fast I had talked, simply because I was interested in the subject about which I was speaking. I forgot that one's voice seems to accelerate when it comes over the air.

Now I try to speak more slowly, but it is not always easy, yet it is something which we can all take trouble over, and study, which I assure you is very well worthwhile.

Something I find distinctly irritating, and I am sure a great number of older people do too, is that they do insist on putting women, or rather pretty young girls, on the television to read the news.

My hearing is not as acute as it was, and I often find it difficult to follow everything they say because their voices are too high.

A man's voice is much easier – and it is important we should be able to hear all the news. I am sure there are millions of men and women of the same age as myself who want to complain.

It is, however, quite normal that as you grow older it becomes more difficult to hear high notes, and the squeak of a bat is lost for ever!

But men's voices, I am delighted to repeat, are easier to hear, and in general anyway, men speak very much more clearly and slowly than women.

While I am talking about voices, if you have trouble with your throat there is something you can do immediately.

Mix a little honey with some warm water and gargle with it for several minutes and you will be amazed at the difference it makes to your voice.

Some people advocate ordinary salt, by which I hope they mean sea salt, which you can buy in a Healthfood Store. This is also quite effective, but I find honey better than anything.

Also exciting are Propolis Lozenges, which I talk in detail about later in the book, and which you should always have with you if you are going into a crowded place where people are either sneezing over you, or are likely to give you influenza germs.

Propolis Lozenges are delicious so children love them, and because they are made of honey they have an instant effect on catarrh and on a sore throat.

Elizabeth Gunning was so poor when she arrived from Ireland with her sister that the two girls had only one dress between them and if one went to a ball the other had to stay at home.

Elizabeth, twice a Duchess, washed in rain water, which she had learnt when in Ireland improved the skin, and because her first husband the Duke of Hamilton drank, she seldom touched alcohol.

Having put men and women on the right path towards a new youth, out of the blue I found something so fantastic as a rejuvenator that I can hardly believe it really exists.

It comes from Texas and it is called Super Oxide Dismutase, which has been conveniently shortened to SOD.

Experts, I am told, have been working on it for a long time and it really is a 'Youth Pill' in two remarkable ways. First it makes anyone who takes it look and feel up to 20 or 30 years younger by firming their skin, smoothing their wrinkles and boosting their energy supply. Secondly, this amazing natural substance, and enzyme, slows down the ageing process and gives you a longer and healthier life.

'SOD may turn into a major breakthrough in health and ageing,' declared Dr Richard Cutler, a research chemist at the USA's National Institute of Ageing. 'Our studies show that it's an exciting find. It certainly suggests strongly that SOD plays a role in retarding ageing and promoting a long life.'

Dr Martin Feldman – a leading New York neurologist and nutrition specialist – enthused: 'SOD is an exciting and effecting way to stay younger and feel better. You look years younger – very much younger. It can make people in their 40s look as if they're in their 20s, while people in the 60s can look more like 35 or 40!'

He continued by saying that in two or three weeks after you have begun taking SOD you will feel an increased sense of well-being and become fatigued less easily. Within a few months there will be noticeable physical changes.

I took some optimistically, but was not certain it would work until in 1982 I went to New York as the 'Queen of Romance of the World'.

At a very large banquet I was taken to luncheon by the best-looking man I have ever seen. He looked like one of 'my Dukes'. He was about six foot in height, slim, dark and handsome. Naturally, as soon as we sat down I asked him: 'What do you do?'

'I have just finished my fourth book on the White House on which I am an expert,' he replied, 'and I have a play coming on in the West End.'

I must have looked rather surprised, for he looked too young to have done so much, and he said with a smile: 'How old do you think I am?'

I thought about 25, but as that was rather young to have written four books, I said: 'To tell you the truth, 35.'

He laughed and said: 'I am 55!'

My son, who is 10 years younger was furious – he looked so marvellous!

'How do you do it?' I asked.

'I have been taking SOD for three years,' he replied.

When I went to the rostrum to speak I made him stand up and show himself to the audience, and they were far more interested in SOD than in my talking about Romance.

The result was that it sold out in every Healthfood Store in that part of New York, and the pharmacists kept asking what had happened that so many people were demanding it.

The same thing happened in England when I came back and told everybody about SOD.

I can only quote Dr Richard Brennan of Houston, Texas, founder of the International Academy of Preventative Medicine, who said: 'Within weeks of taking SOD people look younger, their skin will have a better colour and their bodies will become trimmer and more youthful. The wrinkles and lines on their faces begin to disappear. I've used it on over 1,000 patients. It is very definitely an anti-ageing substance that slows down degenerative diseases.'

I am proving it on myself, and I can honestly say that I do feel better, I am doing more work than I have done for a long time, and my sons and anybody else to whom I have given SOD, are tremendously impressed.

Now, I am glad to say, it is available in all Healthfood Stores, both in Britain and America and of course, at the Health and Happiness Club in Cranleigh, Surrey, England.

Another thing has just appeared on the Health market which I find fantastic. This is Octacosanol, which was developed to help athletes but is also a tremendous help to anyone getting older. It is on sale in the UK or USA.

Octacosanol is a natural food substance which is present in wheat germ. It is a part of Vitamin E which research scientists have for a long time looked for.

It was Professor Cureton who discovered the critical unknown factor in wheat germ and wheatgerm oil was Octacosanol. Since then it has been discovered that this substance helps energy to be released, and it can have a fantastic effect on those who take it. In improving strength and endurance, it also stimulates the transfer of oxygen from the blood to the muscles, strengthening them and preventing fatigue.

It is exactly what every athlete has prayed for.

It has also been shown that Octacosanol improves stamina and also reaction time.

I find that Octacosanol gives me energy every day without feeling tension of any sort: just a feeling of well-being and happiness.

I think as we grow older we all need Octacosanol, especially if we are engaged either in work which requires concentration or in any form of physical activity.

In case you think things like Octacosanol and the other products I have told you about are just a 'flash in the pan', thought up overnight, let me say that I believe you would be quite right to be frightened of that sort of tonic.

But experimental research was carried out by scientists both on animals and on human beings for no less than 23 years before the conclusion was reached that Octacosanol constituted an active biological factor which would improve stamina, strength and reaction time.

I will not bore you with more facts and figures, except to tell you that I have read them and I think they are extremely impressive. The tests were carried out on hundreds of people, including members of the US National Swimming, Wrestling and Track Athletic Teams, physical education undergraduates, middle-aged men, young boys and the US Navy and Marine Corps Demolition Teams.

If all those people say it is fantastic and marvellous, I do not think any of us can go wrong in taking it every day.

I, personally, find it difficult now to be without it.

One of the most fascinating rejuvenating products in the whole of the Health Movement, because it has such an exciting history, is Fo-Ti Tieng, now available in the UK and the USA. I remember first hearing about this herb in the Thirties, which must have been about the time Professor Menier, who studied it in Paris, died. It only came back into our existence a short time ago, and then at last we had the whole story of this remarkable elixir of life.

It is found only in certain jungle districts of the Eastern Tropics. Professor Menier claimed to have found an unknown vitamin which he termed 'Vitamin X'. This appeared to have a marvellous rejuvenating effect on the brain cells and endocrine glands.

In China, Fo-Ti Tieng gained its popularity through the fact that a very well-known Chinese herbalist, Li Chung Yun, lived to be 256 years of age after taking this herb every day.

Professor Li Chung Yun was born in 1677 and the *New York Times* announced his death in 1933, saying his life-span had reached over two and a half centuries. His age was officially recorded by the Chinese Government and confirmed by the head of Chang-Tu University.

Credibility was given to the Professor's amazing age by the fact that he had outlived 23 wives and was living with Number 24 at the time of his death.

'The Dreamer of Songs', co-star with Bob Hope and Bing Crosby in Road to Singapore. *Her philosophy makes her a happy person and she also gives happiness everywhere she goes.*

'I try to keep young through positive thinking and getting involved in numerous projects, mostly theatrical. I don't worry about every wrinkle. I'm a senior citizen and I'm proud of it.'

He gave a course of 28 lectures on longevity at the Chinese University, each of which lasted for three hours. He was then over 200 years old!

Those who saw him declared that he did not look older than a man of 52. He stood straight and strong, and had his own hair and teeth.

They claimed at the time, and it has been repeated continually since, that Li Chung Yun's long life was due to his strict vegetarian diet, his calm serene attitude towards life, and that he regularly used two powerful rejuvenating herbs in his tea. One of them was Fo-Ti Tieng, the other was Ginseng.

With the exception of the Ginseng root Li would not eat anything that had not been produced above ground.

After clinical tests of Fo-Ti Tieng had been made over an extensive period, its rejuvenating qualities made such an impression that the French Government financed a scientific study of living plants before eventually establishing an experimental station in Algeria. (A research foundation in connection with a college in Colombo, Sri Lanka, received an endorsement from the British Government for the same purpose.)

A French biologist, Jules Lépine, conducted an examination and found that the leaves and seeds yielded a very rare tonic property which has a marked energizing effect on nerves and brain cells. Like Professor Menier, he too was excited by the discovery of what appeared to be a new vitamin not known in any other food or herb. This he and his colleagues described as 'Youth Vitamin X'.

An interesting sidelight was thrown upon this unique vitamin by the assertion many years ago of Nanddo Narian, an Indian sage then 107 years old, to the effect that Fo-Ti Tieng provided the missing ingredient in a man's diet without which he can never wholly control disease and decay.

There are, as we all know, people striving to find the elixir of life. Ponce de Léon sought restoration of youth from the waters of a charmed fountain in Florida, the Kintan of the Chinese, the Red Elixir of Geber and the Vital Essence of Augsburg.

The Bolivian Indians made an elixir out of a thornless cactus which, it is said, had the power of keeping men young right up to their death, while not so long ago a Swiss named Spalinger claimed to have found a serum that prolonged life to 150 years.

Personally I am a great believer in Fo-Ti Tieng – but I say this rather nervously for I have no wish to live for 256 years.

Another product that is quite new and which has appeared on the Health market, comes from China.

Ling Chih is known as a miraculous plant, a mushroom, a member of the family of fungi, one of the most precious and rare medicinal plants in China.

The people of China say that Ling Chih has the virtue of raising the dead and giving them life again. The 'Chinese *Materia Medica'*, a pharmacopoeia by a world-famous pharmacologist Li Shih-Chen, justifies this valuation of ancient times and asserts: 'Ling Chih strengthens the heart, increases vitality, and mental activity, and guards against forgetfulness. A regular dose of the medicine keeps one nimble and wholesome, and preserves one's youthful complexion.'

It contains a variety of different things, a great number of enzymes, and is prepared, I am told, through strictly scientific processes. It is not unpleasant to take, if one puts a spoonful in a little water and drinks it three times a day.

The Chinese say that taken as prescribed it will keep one always healthy and strong, preserve one's high complexion and assure one's longevity.

Ling Chih is available at the moment combined with very special Royal Jelly. A great number of people in the Health Movement are starting to make it, and I think we shall soon be able to have it in many different forms.

One more thing I have been told about it is that it accelerates the blood circulation, dispels fatigue, which is true I have found, safeguards the liver and is efficacious in neurasthenia and chronic bronchitis.

This latter property is important to a great number of people.

Before I discuss the rejuvenation and prevention of ageing products any further, I want to talk about Selenium.

It has only very recently been discovered that if we want to maintain good health and increase our resistance to disease we must have a certain amount of the mineral Selenium in our diet.

Many people have not heard of this essential mineral, and it is only now, after an enormous amount of research by scientists in America, that its importance has been realized.

Selenium is in the soil but chemical fertilizers and other non-organic agricultural practices have generally reduced the content of it even in areas where the soil once contained enough of this vital element.

Selenium has been linked with cancer prevention. Some American scientists now content that its use could reduce breast cancer to 80 per cent of its present level. They have also produced statistics intended to show that where there is little or no Selenium in the soil, there is more cancer and more heart disease. Selenium is now available in Healthfood Stores throughout Britain and the United States.

Selenium, the Americans insist, protects animals from getting cancer. And it is most beneficial when added to the diet of cancer-prone patients.

Research has also shown that the heart muscles require Selenium, and that animals deficient in it develop heart disease very similar to that of humans.

Still acting at 83, with the fascination and charm that captivated London and New York when she stopped the show in both cities in Bitter Sweet. The same Star Quality shows the moment she walks on to the stage. It will always be hers.

'The Alexander Technique and Yoga have helped me wonderfully in Mental and Physical development over the years.

Plus a quotation made by Marcus Aurelius:

"Our life is simply what our thoughts make it." So I just try to always think young.'

It has been proved – and I think this is very important – that Selenium supplements reduce tissue damage incurred during heart attacks and help to regulate the blood pressure.

A lot of people tell me that for them Selenium reduces heart pain. What is also very significant and very helpful is to learn that Selenium is essential for reproduction. In fact, it is said that without it one finds not only infertility but a depression of sexual vitality and drive.

The Americans, who carry out their research very thoroughly and spend a great deal of money on it, have discovered that local birth rates in the United States seem to be directly proportional to the level of Selenium in the diet.

This all adds up to the fact that if you have enough Selenium – but not too much – you will live longer and remain younger than you do without it.

The daily requirement for ordinary, healthy people is 50–150 μg, while to prevent or help any of the diseases I have mentioned, 200–300 μg may be prescribed.

Foods which generally contain Selenium are meat – chicken, lamb and pork – fish, shellfish, grains, cereals, fruits and vegetables. But to obtain a large amount of Selenium from these foods would require one to eat an enormous amount, so it is easier to take one or two Selenium tablets a day, depending on their strength. If, however, you are going to buy Selenium tablets from your Healthfood Store, I think it is essential to look at the label on the tablets first to make quite certain that the ones you buy have yeast as an additional ingredient. The element is more effective when combined with yeast.

Another important addition to Selenium tablets is Vitamin E. I have always said that Vitamin E is the most essential vitamin, because it helps us in so many different ways.

Given all the various clinical evidence, it is obvious that we should be very stupid if we did not realize the tremendous importance of Selenium, plus yeast and Vitamin E.

I give Selenium ACE to all my family. A few months ago my adorable white Pekingese Twi-Twi developed a small cancer on his behind. He is now 13 years old and the only living dog who has ever been in Madame Tussaud's. He is also the main character in my novel *The Prince and the Pekingese*.

The Vet operated on Twi-Twi and a week later he came back to see how he was. 'I have never known a dog heal so quickly!' he exclaimed in astonishment.

'I gave Twi-Twi Selenium ACE,' I explained.

Now the Vet is taking it!

Honey heals, rejuvenates and gives
those who take it beauty and virility.
Taken reguarly before going to bed –
two large teaspoonfuls with a
teaspoonful or cider vinegar, mixed
into a tumbler of water – will help you
to sleep.

14

People have been trying to find the Secret of Life since the beginning of time.

According to the Bible, Methuselah lived 969 years, and more recently a Russian fruit farmer who died in 1973 was said to be 168. There was also a Mrs Khafaf Lazuria who was thought to be the oldest woman in the world until she died in 1973, at the age of 139.

The more I read about these people – and there are quite a number of others – the more I realize that almost all of them lived the most boring lives in some obscure part of the world.

So I cannot help feeling that half the modern people who are struggling with crash diets, Health Farms, counting calories and trying a new treatment every week to keep their youth, would perhaps do much better to have a short, amusing life, rather than struggling vainly against old age!

I have often longed for them to smile at their earnest endeavours and treat the whole thing as a laugh.

C. B. Cochran, who gave us all the world-famous stars of the Twenties and Thirties, used to tell a funny story about the funeral of Harry Tate, a great comedian at the beginning of the century.

One of the mourners was Charles Coburn, another comedian. 'How old are you, Charlie?' an actor asked him in the cemetery.

'Eighty-nine,' Charlie answered.

'Hardly worth going home, is it!' the questioner replied.

How do you want to be remembered when you leave this life?

I was reading one of Cecil Beaton's *Diaries* the other day. He was an old friend from the Twenties and I always admired his iron-willed struggle to succeed.

He wrote of various old people in a way I found very revealing. Of one of our great novelists he said:

June 8th 1970

'E. M. Forster died yesterday aged ninety-two. He was a sweet man, gentle, self-effacing, kind, with great moral courage and a determination to fight for what he believed in.'

The beautiful Lady Diana Cooper captivated him, as she still does everyone, although she is over 90.

August 1970

'Diana Cooper is lying on her bed. Her broken leg has hurt her so much . . .
What bearing she shows, always pulling her weight, never complaining . . . I
realise how unique she is, for she's nearing eighty.'

Of Cathleen Nesbitt, the actress, he writes:

'She is generous, kind and unselfish and she has an inner contentment. It is
incredible to believe she is eighty-two years old. Her brain is still quick and
alert and her ability to quote at great length from poetry and literature is
impressive. She is wonderfully beautiful – she leaps out of bed, runs upstairs
and does exercises like a child. Without much luxury she manages to be
delightfully dressed. She is the perfect example of how to grow old, and prove
how wrong it is to make too much effort in the ways of artifice.'

The appreciation I enjoy most was written about the 'Yellow Earl'. This was
the 5th Earl of Lonsdale who, when I was young, was the most flamboyant
and fantastic member of the aristocracy.

A great sportsman, he was cheered on every race-course and no one could
miss him because his cars, his carriages and racing colours were yellow, and
he always wore a yellow carnation in his buttonhole.

Another personality at every race meeting was an eccentric black tipster
who called himself 'Prince Monolulu'.

Among the wreaths at the Earl's funeral in 1944 was one with a card which
read:

LORD LONSDALE

Great Britain's Greatest Ambassador of Clean Sport
Boxing, Wrestling, Swimming, Yachting,
All Ball Games,
Man's Friend, the Dog his delight.
'A Horse, A Horse.' The Pillar of the Turf.
'A Horse, A Horse.' The Friend of the Friendless.
An African Negro prays that your Spirit, like
John Brown's song, will go marching on
'In Glory, Glory Hallelujah'.
That all Mankind will be Brothers through
Clean Sport.

RAS PRINCE MONOLULU

When I was young I remember all the excitement there was about Vorloff's treatment, which involved transplanting monkey glands. There were thousands of jokes about it, and it was soon found that any improvements that were noted were only temporary, and in some cases imaginary.

Then there was a wild excitement about Professor Paul Niehans who injected cells from the fetuses of sheep into patients who then declared they were given fuller and longer lives without any of the unpleasant ageing process.

The Professor's patients were reported to have included Charles de Gaulle, the Duke and Duchess of Windsor, General Eisenhower, the Japanese Imperial Family, Marlene Dietrich, Charlie Chaplin, and Pope Pius XII who publicly blessed the treatment.

Having known some of these famous people I cannot say that I saw any amazing improvement in them, and Professor Niehans himself died in his early 70s.

After Niehans came a great friend of mine, Professor Ana Aslan, from Bucharest. She arrived in London in 1959 and lunched with me at Camfield Place. Like everybody else, I was astounded at how young and energetic she was in her 60s. She certainly looked barely 40, and I was thrilled to try her treatment Gerovital H3, later to be known as GH3.

Ana Aslan remained a friend for many years. She gave me her treatment, but I cannot honestly say that I saw any fantastic alteration in my health or looks although I was longing to do so.

All the same, she herself was obviously a walking advertisement and Dr Hugh Johnson, 'The Red Dean of Canterbury' who visited her clinic when he was in Bucharest, said: 'The treatment has had an extraordinary happy effect on me, restoring powers I had lost. It has made me feel and act as if several years had been taken off my age.'

After that, a great number of people rushed to the Rumanian State Institute of Geriatrics in Bucharest, which promptly became known as the Aslan Clinic for Rejuvenation.

The Duke of Bedford was one patient, the Begum Aga Khan another, and in 1974 Ana Aslan said that with the help of her miracle drug GH3, a person might be able to live for 130 years! GH3 is still available in the UK and USA.

But all these different treatments became rather overshadowed when Ginseng was discovered, and was found to give people cheaply and effectively at home the energy and feeling of well-being they long to find.

Before this, however, Pollen had come to the fore. This particularly interested me, as it is what honey is made from.

I actually went to Sweden and met the 'King of Pollen' who had patented a way of extracting it from a field of clover, and I saw half-a-million pounds'

A Star who glitters on the screen and off. No one will ever forget her brilliance in The Wicked Lady.

'I've never had beauty treatments, never taken much exercise, and very seldom gone on a diet. Never burning the candle at both ends and being a life-long teetotaller may have something to do with it.

My doctor once told me that my lack of energy and needing plenty of sleep were due to my low blood pressure.

Perhaps it can be summed up by "young at heart" – I am sure that applies to you.'

worth of Pollen stacked in a shed waiting to be sent all over the world.

Pollen in various forms, such as Pollen-B, undoubtedly helps a large number of people suffering from various complaints. It soon became a popular energy booster and stamina builder among British athletes and sportsmen. Many of the peak performances achieved at the Commonwealth Games in 1974 were said to be due to widespread consumption of Pollen.

And so it seems to me that we have come full circle to what is really the most magical food in the world and undoubtedly an 'Elixir of Youth' – and that is Honey, in whatever shape or form it comes.

At the same time the search goes on, and what is important is for people to have hope and faith.

It is really true that faith can move mountains, and just as we all know people that can die because they give up hope and no longer wish to go on living, so one can live longer and more fully in the hope and faith that one can do so.

What I know I give to the people who write to me from all over the world, is the knowledge that there is usually a cure for what they are suffering from. It is a natural one which comes from Nature herself, and not from a chemical factory, and that they can heal themselves if they believe sufficiently in what they are doing.

This is the faith that is ageless, and has come down to us from the very beginning of time.

Of course, as I said at the beginning of this book, our bodies will wear out. That is inevitable, and it is very stupid to cling to a suit of clothes that is old, ragged, threadbare and no longer of any use.

But Life cannot die and therefore all that we have acquired in this lifetime, all we have learnt, all we have suffered and made sacrifices to attain is still ours.

That is the wonder and glory of Life. That is what Christ, Buddha, Mohammed and all the great spiritual leaders since the beginning of time have tried to teach us.

You can call it Resurrection, the Wheel of Rebirth or Reincarnation – it does not matter what expression is used. The undeniable truth is that nothing is lost, nothing is thrown away.

YOUR talents, YOUR powers and YOU YOURSELF are ETERNAL.

For thinning hair take Vitamin E and move the scalp gently.

Cod liver oil, taken every morning in a small amount of milk, softens the skin and prevents wrinkles.

15

Having told you how to rejuvenate yourself and live for ever I think it very important that we should consider the aches and pains of old age which undoubtedly occur in everyone, however hard we may try to avoid them.

What I have found in the years I have been working on health, however, is that there is a natural cure for practically everything.

As it is almost unknown for any of the things I recommend to have an adverse reaction, I do beg of you to try them before you start out on the perilous path of antibiotics which may have terrible side-effects.

Remember that all the 'chemicalized' medicines break down one's resistance to other illnesses.

A doctor working in a London hospital told me five years ago that 10 per cent of the beds in his hospital were filled with patients who were suffering from the side-effects of drugs and antibiotics which they had taken to cure something else.

I personally find this terrifying! And I had a very bitter experience myself to prove it.

I never, never take antibiotics because quite frankly, I am frightened of them! But four years ago I had influenza and was feeling very low just as I had some very important engagements with people who were coming over from America to see me.

My son kept saying to me: 'Hurry up and get well! There is so much for you to do. You can't possibly be ill at the moment!' But I was feeling rotten. The local doctor was coming in to see one of my staff who was also ill, and I told her how I was feeling.

'I have to get well quickly!' I said.

She laughed and said: 'Here's something which will help you. It's not really an antibiotic, or rather a very, very mild one, and you will be on your feet in no time.'

Very stupidly, and simply because I was feeling desperate, I took the capsule. The next morning the doctor came in again to ask how I was and I said: 'I feel a little better, but one of my eyes is out of focus.'

'Nonsense!' she said. 'You are just imagining it!'

But what had happened was that I had got fluid behind the eye, and as it was something I have never had before – and although it has moved a little in the last three years I still have a black spot on the right side of my eye – I am absolutely convinced it is due to taking *one* antibiotic.

That is why I am now going to give you a list of almost everything you are likely to have wrong with you, and to beg you at least to try a natural treatment.

Let me make it very clear that all the vitamins and other products I have mentioned are *not* to be found in pharmacies but in Healthfood Stores (or the Health and Happiness Club in Cranleigh, Surrey, England).

Anaemia

Many people when they get old suffer from the shortage of red blood cells known as anaemia. Fortunately we have a complete cure for it in a product marketed in the UK and the USA under the brand-name Floradix, which is the only iron tonic I know that does not have any side-effects.

We have been saying for ages that iron tonics upset the system in so many different ways that people will do anything rather than take them.

One woman I know told me that when she was pregnant she was so upset by the iron she was told to take for anaemia that she felt she could not continue having the baby. When I gave her Floradix she could hardly believe the difference.

And as for anaemic children, I know from my grandchildren that they find it delicious to take, and so there are no difficulties in that way.

Floradix is a liquid, which again is an advantage for those who through being old, find it hard to swallow pills or capsules.

It is certainly a great mistake to be anaemic. Here is a simple test you can do yourself. If the inside of your lower eye-lid is white and so are your gums, then you need Floradix.

Arthritis and Rheumatism

Arthritis is a 'Bogey Man' to all old people, and what is so terrible in Britain is that they are quite surprised if they *don't* have it.

One reason, I am absolutely convinced, is that such rheumatic disorders often begin because British people never remember to air their clothes properly. Even in a household with new appliances, sheets are often put on the bed while they are still damp, and clothes which have been washed are expected to dry in our over-moist atmosphere then to be worn when they are not really dry enough to prevent us catching a cold from them.

Worse than colds, arthritis and rheumatism are very difficult to get rid of, and it is very important to prevent them.

People are very stupid about airing. All one has to do is to have one of those fireproof electric radiators put into a cupboard, and after the sheets and clothes have been stored there for 24 hours they are completely dry; there is no chance of anybody suffering from their dampness.

I am particularly fussy about drying pillow-cases, because a stiff neck caused by a damp pillow-case can result in rheumatism which is hard to remove.

Arthritis has been suffered by humans and animals since the beginning of time.

Some years ago when a new road was being constructed on part of my husband's moor in Scotland, a bulldozer unearthed the body of a Chieftain's daughter, who had been buried in pre-Viking days. Although she had been quite young when she died, the doctors found signs of arthritis on the bones of her skeleton.

I started what has been a terrible saga of pain and discomfort when in February 1974 I fell down in the Taj Mahal by moonlight! Everybody laughs when I tell them this, but actually from my viewpoint it was a disaster.

The Taj Mahal is the most beautiful, the most romantic, the most spiritual and esoteric monument in the world, and I have seen it at every time of the day, but perhaps it is more beautiful at night than at any other time. The gateway into it has a very high step, and on this occasion the Indians instead of shining their torches on our feet shone them in our faces.

I caught my toe on the step and fell forward, making the front of my leg bleed rather badly, but what I did not realize at the time was that I had put out the base of my spine. This pressed on the sciatic nerve, and in a month's time I was in agony.

I then started the lengthy business of trying to find somebody to help me. I went to six osteopaths, I had traction – which the Christians invented for the Infidels – and I had acupuncture! I had injections! I took dozens of different so-called cures for rheumatism, arthritis, sciatica and gout!

None of them really helped, and the only suggestion I had from doctors was that I should have a surgical operation to cut off the end of the spine. This I was determined not to have done, for I understand that the operation is seldom successful.

I was becoming really desperate, and had reached the stage where I couldn't walk more than a few yards and it was very painful to turn over in bed. In fact, to do the latter I had to pull my legs round using both hands.

Then a friend told me that on television she had seen Ludovic Kennedy

One of the greatest natural baritones of the century. He has also conquered the musical theatre and has received every accolade the United States can bestow.

'My interesting analogy and advice to young people is that if one is going to succeed and stay young, one has to establish a strong discipline and regime in early life which will carry one forward into maturing years. I maintain that one should have many interests besides one's career so that at certain times in life one's attention can be directed into them to keep one from getting stale.

I have always been a devotee of yoga and have kept a strict dietary regime all of my life. Of course, no cigarettes. Twelve years ago I gave up eating meat and dairy products and restrict myself to a diet of broiled chicken and fresh fish. My family on both sides all died young, therefore I feel that my strict dietary schedule will give me greater longevity.

I am devoted to vitamins B and C in all categories, and not only disapprove of any type of tranquillizer, but have never taken an aspirin!'

interview a man called Bruce MacManaway, who did marvellous things with bad backs. I had nothing to lose, so I wrote to him at the BBC, and asked if he ever came to London, as I understood he lived in Scotland.

He rang up and gave me an appointment, and I had no idea he was a healer until I arrived at his mother's flat and met the most charming and delightful old lady of 80 who told me she had herself been a healer for 30 years.

'I worked very hard to help people,' she said, 'and I never took money for it. But my son has a wife and three children, and as he has left the Army to continue his work, he has to charge a small fee.'

It was in fact a very small fee, but as soon as I met Major MacManaway I felt that he had very special powers. I learnt later that he had discovered his power of healing in 1940 and later, with his wife, founded the Westlake Healing and Teaching Centre.

To my great relief I did not have to undress. I merely sat in front of him and he put his hands on my spine and with a very small movement put the 'tail' which was out of place back into its proper position.

'Now I am going to put on the heat,' he said.

I could feel waves of heat going up my back which vibrated all over my body. Only when he had finished did I realize it was his hands alone which had produced the heat!

From that moment my spine was in the correct place – but I had terrible adhesions of arthritis from the 18 months in which I had been incapacitated.

I read Adele Davis's book *Let's Get Well*, and found that for arthritis she recommends Calcium Pantothenate, which is a new way of taking Pantothenic acid, one of the B vitamins. She wrote that deficiencies in this vitamin have been known to produce one or more of the following symptoms: fatigue, listlessness, digestive disturbances, headaches, irritability, heaviness, mental depression, quarrelsomeness and recurring respiratory infections.

She also said that Calcium Pantothenate removes the pain and the stiffness of arthritis. This was something I had never heard of before so I rang round the Health Movement to find out where I could get it. At that time they came in tablets containing 25 mg each, whereas now they are available in other dosages, in both the UK and the USA.

Immediately I took them, the pains in my leg and ankle felt better and it was easier to walk. I was then told that a certain doctor, E. C. Barton-Wright, had been working on Calcium Pantothenate for some years with the most fantastic results.

Of course few people had been told about it, for doctors never advertise their findings until their research is completed. (Later I discovered that one could have a variety of injections for arthritis.)

In two months I was free of all pain and could walk quite normally.

Recent scientific findings show that a major factor in arthritis is a deficiency of Pantothenic acid. Osteoarthritis in dogs, especially in pedigree animals, has been increasing during the last 10 to 15 years, possibly through feeding these animals on highly processed canned foods.

Dr Barton-Wright and his colleague Dr Elliott achieved remarkable results with people who were vegetarian arthritics. When patients were injected with a mixture of Royal Jelly and Calcium Pantothenate, many showed a rapid disappearance of the symptoms – in 14 days – with a remarkable increase in the blood level of Pantothenic acid.

Another doctor has suggested that if pregnant women were prescribed 50 mg of Pantothenic acid daily, it might prevent a number of miscarriages.

Both rheumatoid arthritis and osteoarthritis are on the increase the world over, and there is no doubt that this is due to the world's insistence on eating more and more highly preserved foods which, as we in the Health Movement are well aware, are dangerous.

Arthritis is an insidious disease and may take many years before visible symptoms appear.

We are all of us eating some Pantothenic acid in our diet, inadequate though the amount may be, but it is my advice that anyone who feels any twinges of pain from rheumatism, gout or any other allied disease – which means practically everyone – would be wise immediately to take at least 50 mg of Calcium Pantothenate a day.

Since I cured myself with Calcium Pantothenate, quite a lot of different treatments have appeared which we had never heard of before.

One of the most effective supplements discovered is 'Devil's Claw'. This is the nickname given by the sheep farmers of the Leonardville area in Namibia to a *Harpagophytum* plant because it has barbed hooks on the outgrowth of its seed which catch in the wool of their sheep.

A visitor from Africa told me that Devil's Claw has been known for centuries to the Africans who are convinced that it has healing properties, some of which border on the miraculous. It cures their stomach ailments, malaria, and many women's complaints.

He went on to relate that at one time South African women who had skin cancer were healed by an application of Devil's Claw ointment. Infused as tea, it helped mothers to give easier birth. But it was only after an absence of many years, and because of heavy rain during one season that the flower of the *Harpagophytum* began growing prolifically again. It was by remarking the enthusiasm of the natives that the outside world began to be interested.

The handsome Royal Photographer w[...] makes every woman as beautiful as [...] dreams.

'Sleep and energy go hand in hand – you cannot have one without the other, particularly as you get on a bit.

Sleep like money can be banked. Try taking a week off work and sleep for twelve hours a night or longer, you then will find that your energy stays up on very little sleep for a month subsequently.

Never lure sleep with pills. If you can't get to sleep, change from coffee to weak tea, because you also bank caffeine.

I have found there are two other effective ways of preparing for sleep without drugs.

Fill a bath one foot deep with cold water, walk up and down in it for two minutes slowly, wiggle your toes, dab your feet dry and jump into bed.

Then breathe in the slowest possible, hold it for ten seconds, breathe out slowly again, repeat several times.

Finally, never take pills for anything, no aspirin, no alka-selzer. If you have a headache you have recently abused your body and it is trying to tell you so.'

The Devil's Claw has a bitter root which grows about an inch thick and penetrates the soil up to three feet deep. It is, in fact, the root which has the magical qualities.

A scientist called Von Korvin-Krasinski studied the root in 1964 after he heard that locally it was used for diseases of the gall bladder, pancreas, stomach and kidneys. It was also lauded as having a beneficial effect on diabetes, diseases of the liver, kidneys, bladder, stomach and intestines.

Devil's Claw is quite cheap in the Healthfood Stores; I have recommended it to many people and taken it myself, and I personally find it quite extra-ordinary. It is available in the UK and the USA.

I have already mentioned Selenium. I have recently heard that the head of the Rheumatoid Arthritis Research Centre is himself taking it, and has found that he can walk much more easily, without the pain in his legs he used to have.

There is also something else to help arthritis sufferers: a form of relief that comes from the sea.

It has only just been appreciated that the sea is teeming with life and vir-tually all known minerals. New Zealand Green Lipped Mussels live and feed in the ocean and, through their special filter mechanism, naturally absorb a high concentration of these nutrients.

A preparation from these Mussels was introduced by the Health Movement (marketed in the UK as Seatone and in the USA as Seacare or Neptone) and found to be so effective that now it is used in a great number of hospitals where the patients benefit almost immediately from what is essentially an entirely natural product.

One word of warning I must give you: that is, if you suffer from rheumatism or arthritis of any sort, do not eat fruit. Many doctors still advocate that patients should try salads and fruit, but my experience is that in the great majority of cases it makes one worse. Fruit is far too acid in every way to be taken for any form of rheumatic pain.

Personally, I have always believed that fruit is only excellent when you eat it in the country to which it belongs, and even apples can be dangerous in England when we know they are sprayed with arsenic to keep away bugs.

I never recommend orange juice or any citrus juices at any time; they are too strong not only for teeth but also for our very delicate stomachs. Many people have found that their habitual indigestion stems from drinking citrus juice.

I have to say here – although many people who have orange juice for break-fast will be furious – the proof of what I have just written can be found in the *Health Finder* published by Rodale, who have gone deeply into the research on this controversial subject.

From my own experience, any fruit can make most forms of rheumatism more painful than it is already. Moreover, I am far too careful of my teeth to risk endangering them with anything that is as questionable as oranges, grapefruits or pineapples.

Asthma

One of my sons has had asthma for years and also the bad eczema which often goes with it. He tried every sort of cure: ointments, pills and creams, but nothing seemed to help him for long until a product was brought out (marketed in the UK under the brand-name Efamol) which contains oil extracted from the seeds of the evening primrose together with safflower oil and linseed oil. These are an excellent source of the polyunsaturates we know to be so vital for normal metabolism. Vitamin E is also added to prevent the oxidization of unsaturated fats and to help stabilize the essential fatty acids in the oil. But, perhaps of more importance, the Evening Primrose Oil contained in Efamol is the richest natural source of one particular substance which is currently the centre of considerable scientific interest. This is GLA (gamma linolenic acid).

GLA is useful for maintaining our normal cholesterol levels, regulating our blood pressure, and ensuring the free flow of blood platelets through the arteries. All this helps to ensure a healthy skin as well as controlling the menstrual cycle.

It is hard to believe that there is generally no GLA present in our diet and therefore, as we grow older, we are more and more in need of something of the kind to balance the cholesterol in our bodies.

A preparation containing GLA is a very easy way to take something which has a marvellous effect on so many different bodily functions. One of the most important of these is to have a free flow of blood, another is to regulate the blood pressure, and both of these are absolutely vital to older people, especially if they are less active than they used to be.

As I have said, Efamol has helped my son's skin and eczema, and is definitely making increasingly longer the intervals between his attacks of asthma.

I had finished writing this when my hairdresser, Ann Austen, who travels with me on my promotional appearances, told me that her mother who has diabetes, has been taking Efamol on my advice. 'The most extraordinary thing,' Mrs Austen said, 'is that my mother's rheumatism, which was very painful in her hands and legs, cleared up completely after she had taken Efamol for under a week. I could hardly believe it!'

Blood Pressure

Blood pressure is a problem, I have found, in almost everybody over 40.

I had very low blood pressure for many years, and thought it was a good thing until I discovered that you can just as easily have a stroke from having low blood pressure as you can from having high. There were also times when I was very tired, and felt as if I was walking through water.

This happened to me almost immediately after the War, and the doctors struggled with every sort of treatment to try to regulate my blood pressure.

Then I took estrogen (marketed as it is in the UK as Premarin) as Hormone Replacement Therapy, and overnight my blood pressure became normal.

It was so astonishing – it is not a standard reaction at all – that nobody could believe it, but it has remained more or less stable ever since, except occasionally when it gets a little high.

When this happens, I take a very effective treatment of Garlic, Hawthorn, and Mistletoe in capsule form. These are so good that a friend with very high blood pressure told me that after only three weeks' treatment, to the astonishment of his doctors, his blood pressure became absolutely normal. He swore that he was going to take these capsules every day for the rest of his life!

Each contains: 70 mg extract from 361.71 mg Hawthorn flowers, leaves and fruits; 30 mg Mistletoe extract from 180 mg Mistletoe Herb; and 78 mg Garlic-Oil maceration (1:1).

I think garlic is very important to our diet; the effect of garlic in preventing colds and 'flu is useful besides its help for the blood pressure.

The Brilliant Brain

I said at the beginning of this book that I was working on the brain.

Fortunately I have considerable assistance from two outstanding products.

One is an 'old friend', one is new. The 'older' one, which I call the 'Brain Pill' for short, has helped me enormously for some years, as it has a great number of other people. It is marketed in the UK under the brand-name Celaton CH3 Tri-Plus and in the USA as Celaton V.

Its manufacturers tell me they have continual requests now from company directors because when their health staffs administer it as a tonic to all their workers, they find the volume of work increases and everybody manages to work more cheerfully and regularly because they feel so well.

I gave Celaton CH3 Tri-Plus to Gloria Hunniford, Britain's latest and most successful radio and television reporter, and she tells me that it has had a tremendous effect on her capacity for work. Both my grown-up grandsons told me they found it marvellous when they were doing examinations; one is now a chartered accountant, the other has been called to the Bar.

Everybody who tried the Brain Pill tells me the same story, and I only wish doctors would seem more aware of its really marvellous properties.

Something newly available in the USA and Britain is PC which is short for Phosphatidyl Choline (or Lecithin).

Years ago Linda Clarke said to me: 'No Lecithin, no brain', so I know she will be delighted that we have an absolutely new form of Lecithin which contains the purest phospholipids yet known.

In the clinical tests it seems to me to be the answer for everybody who feels as they grow older that their brain is failing.

A brilliant doctor at the Massachusetts Institute of Technology was the first person to test Lecithin on neurological disorders. He found, significantly – exactly as Linda Clarke had said – that the amount of Lecithin you eat directly affects the chemical activity of the brain.

Now with the development of PC they are sure they have something that amazingly will restore the brain after the patient has become almost senile.

While the researchers have been able to obtain Lecithin of up to 90 per cent purity, the general public until now have been able only to obtain it 25 per cent pure. At last the purer form is available to us all, and I have been reading with the greatest of interest the reports on PC.

Twenty-six so-called 'incurable' patients after several months' treatment with PC showed a remarkable improvement, including a disappearance of digestive problems, increased ability to sleep, loss of physical fatigue and decreased psychological disturbances, and even more important, an improvement in the structure and metabolism of damaged liver cells.

These were very acute, severe cases, but for the average older person who is gradually slowing down in thought, speech and movement, PC has shown, reports say, 'a great increase in fluency so that they are more alert and effective in social interaction'.

Dr Allan Cott, a New York City psychiatrist, has been working with PC on hyperactive children, who have trouble with their concentration and memory. I believe the results are very impressive.

For ordinary people who feel that their memory is bad, that they are forgetful and slow in their reactions, PC is an exciting and important new 'vitamin'.

It is best to take one capsule first thing in the morning on an empty stomach, and I am certain that after a few weeks, perhaps sooner, you will notice an improvement.

Many doctors think that Lecithin can help to cut down the death rate, and there is no doubt that as well as being a nerve tonic and a revitalizer, Lecithin is also a slimming aid because it works to disperse the accumulation of fat in the body.

Unfortunately heart disease in the United Kingdom is increasing. Some 185,000 people are expected to die from heart troubles in Britain during 1984. It is the biggest killer of men over 35, and the chance of a man aged 40 having at least one heart attack before he is 65 is now one in five.

To me this is terrifying, and I do beg every woman who loves her husband to see that he takes one PC capsule every morning before breakfast.

Colds

The UK Prime Minister, Mrs Thatcher, says she takes Vitamin C every day of her life.

Woodrow Wyatt, the political commentator in the *Sunday Mirror*, says he takes 12 g every day, which is fantastic.

I think it is wise during the winter to take 1 g which, usually and conveniently, is one tablet of Vitamin C, as a preventive measure. If I start to develop a cold I rush and immediately take 2 and repeat this every four hours.

I have stopped cold after cold this way.

Do remember that a cold is said to renew itself every four hours and it is essential not to let it get a 'hold' on you. If you feel a bit shivery at night when you go to bed, take two tablets of Vitamin C.

Incidentally, if you want to slim there is nothing more natural or easy than Vitamin C as a supplement to a reduced diet, and it is very much better for you than anything that can be medically prescribed.

As I have said, garlic is also useful for preventing colds.

Constipation

If you have this, the answer is – Bran! I write fully about this under 'Diverticulitis'.

Diverticulitis

It is estimated that 30 per cent of the British and the Americans have some form of diverticulitis, inflammation of the little pouches that form in the intestinal wall of the colon and rectum. I had this terrible disease when I was 72 and was obliged to undergo surgery, which in these circumstances is extremely unpleasant, very unromantic, and really quite frightening in that one may have to have a colostomy after it.

However, I was fortunate enough to be operated on by Sir Edward Muir, who in accordance with his reputation, did miracles! But today most specialists say they do not use the knife, they insist on their patients taking Bran. What therefore everyone should do as they get older is to take at least three tablespoonsful of Bran every day.

One becomes very bored with the monotony of it, but anything in the world is better than having diverticulitis, which firstly is extremely painful, and secondly may result in a very unpleasant operation.

Bran is fibre – it is made up of cereal husks – and a recent report by Dr Dennis Burkitt completely revolutionized the whole thinking on the subject of intestinal treatment.

Dr Burkitt is convinced that the whole reason for a great many illnesses such as diverticultis, appendicitis, ulcerative colitis and cancer of the large bowel, can be attributed to the fact that we do not have enough fibre in our diet. He studied the whole question and has found that many Western diseases stem from the fact that surplus food takes a very long time to pass through the bowel.

In a test it was found that African villagers who ate about 25 g of fibre a day took, between the time of eating and evacuation, 35 hours. English volunteers who ate white bread and white flour took 70 hours.

George III would never see his statesmen or discuss any Royal business until he had been to the lavatory in the morning. No one seems to understand today that to be constipated is tantamount to poisoning oneself.

Dr Burkitt is thus convinced that the removal of the fibre content of wheat flour by modern roller mills which began in 1880–1900 and the addition to our diet of sugar were the worst things that could have happened to us.

If only I had known about fibre when I was young! I take it now with 'live' yoghurt, which is also very good for one. In fact, I think it is a *must* for those who are getting on and wish to keep well.

There are various different yoghurts on the market but I think the most tasty are those that come from France.

America's most distinguished character actress on stage, screen and television. The accolades have never ceased and they never will.

'I have allowed myself no time to think about age, because when you start thinking old, you are old!

As I am a renowned authority on prize black Pugs, they keep me active. Each one has a personality of his own, influenced by the signs of the Zodiac.

I am also busy with my needlepoint, my books about it and my beloved garden.'

Duodenal Ulcer

This is something I hope you will never get, and yet out of the blue the most unlikely people may suddenly develop one.

My husband developed one just before we were due to leave for our annual honeymoon in Paris. It was in fact, the last year of his life, although I did not know that, but I was very anxious that we should not miss our wonderful time together which I know did us so much good.

'It's no use,' he said after he had seen the X-rays. 'I am in pain and I shall not be able to enjoy anything and I won't be able to eat the good food. It's no use going to Paris like that!'

He had been put on what I call 'milk and misery' by the doctors, which is enough to depress anybody.

Two days before we were due to go and were still talking about whether or not we should cancel the trip, I had to speak at a political meeting in Welwyn Garden City, which is quite near to where I live.

When I arrived I said to the young man who greeted me: 'I'm afraid I can't stay very long. My husband has a duodenal ulcer and is not feeling very well. I must get back to him.'

'Duodenal ulcer?' he exclaimed. 'I can certainly help you.'

I looked at him in surprise, and he said: 'I had one, which was so bad that I used to roll on the floor in agony until I was completely cured with something called *De-Nol.'

I later found that this was a UK brand-name for a substance technically described as tri-potassium di-citrato bismuthate – which for the sake of brevity I will continue to call De-Nol.

I already knew that the stomach produces digestive juices which act on the food we eat and break it down into forms that the body can use. Normally the stomach and the duodenum are not themselves attacked by these juices because they have complex protective mechanisms. Sometimes, however, this protective mechanism breaks down, allowing the digestive juices to attack the lining of the stomach or duodenum, resulting in a raw painful area.

By the time I got home from the meeting I had learnt that De-Nol should be taken on an empty stomach, so that the active material in it can get to the ulcer site quickly, clinging to form a protective layer.

Quite simply this can be compared to putting a dressing over a sore place on the skin to prevent further pain and attack. This protective layer stays in place during your meal but needs renewing before the next. Beneath it, the ulcer is able to heal normally, free from any further aggravation.

I was very enthusiastic, but my husband was rather doubtful, although he

*only available in Britain

was prepared to try anything if there was a chance it could help him.

It is absolutely essential that the directions which come with it are followed: generally, as prescribed, De-Nol must be taken on an empty stomach half an hour before each of the main meals, and two hours after the last meal of the day.

From the first moment my husband took the first dose he had no more pain. We went to Paris and although they said it was a mistake to eat rich meals, he ate the delicious French food and drank a little – but not too much – champagne.

When he returned, the doctors could not believe the difference or the fact that while he was taking De-Nol the duodenal ulcer had disappeared.

I have recommended De-Nol to hundreds of people since and I have never met anyone who said it did not work.

I also learnt in the meantime that it is extremely important for us all to take Propolis. Propolis is the resin collected by the bees to seal the part of the hive where the Queen Bee lives and lays her eggs. She is completely protected from bacteria of any sort by Propolis with the result that she lives for 20 years, while the poor little worker bees exist for only 14 months!

In this day and age when there are so many different things that can go wrong with the stomach, and also there is always the fear of ulcers and other intestinal difficulties, the one answer to all these is Propolis.

I could not do without it, although unfortunately I did not know about it until after I had had diverticulitis. My son, who has slight symptoms of the non-inflamed condition diverticulosis, is also very careful to take it every day. It only means swallowing one or two capsules of *Lactose Propolis, and the results are so fantastic that one would be silly to ignore them.

Propolis was used by the Assyrians to heal wounds, inflamed eyes and tumours. The Egyptians recognized its efficiency in embalming their dead. It was virtually forgotten after 400 BC when it was prescribed by the Greeks in the treatment of abscesses and open wounds, although Theophrastous, a celebrated philosopher, in 390 BC gave exact instructions on how and where this resin may be found.

Nothing could be a more natural product and it is entirely due to the brilliant work of Dr Paul Urban in Austria that we now have this amazing product. He had very stringent tests done on Propolis and found it to be one of the most effective natural antibiotics that has ever been discovered!

Doctors took 250 people suffering from stomach ulcers, colitis and severe gastric conditions into the Public Hospital in Klosterneuburg. They were treated with Propolis. No fewer than 244 of them were completely healed within a fortnight.

*a combination of Propolis and the enzyme lactose

After another test in the Ear, Nose and Throat Clinic at Ljubljana, Yugoslavia, Professor Kern spoke with great enthusiasm of the effect of Propolis on patients with inflammation of the throat and oral cavities.

The patients were asked to chew the Propolis Lozenges – which are so delicious that I have great difficulty in keeping them away from my grandchildren who eat them as if they were sweets. As little as six to ten hours after starting the treatment of Propolis 'bonbons', almost all the patients were free of fever, they felt no pain when swallowing and their general condition was very much improved.

The doctors' findings are, I think, extremely interesting. In 15 severe cases, especially with children, they found an improvement had taken place after only a few hours.

In the case of patients suffering from chronic inflammation of the oral cavity and gums, the symptoms of the inflammation were hardly noticeable the following day.

Another test, made by Frau Dr Edith Lauda, is one of the most interesting I have read of for a long time. What the doctor wished to establish was whether Propolis had an antibacterial effect on the human skin. Fifty-nine patients with really bad acne, from which all had been suffering for several years, were treated with Propolis ointment, now obtainable in England.

One patient had been treated unsuccessfully for 30 years by a great number of dermatologists and clinics, and yet after two Propolis treatments the skin was free from inflammation and only very small marks of the acne were visible.

Equally spectacular was the case of the 40-year-old patient who tried every possible treatment for the acne which covered her whole face, and which completely disappeared after two weeks' of treating herself at home with Propolis tincture and ointment!

Twenty-five cases of acne simplex were completely healed at home within a week.

Eyes

Almost the first thing that people start to worry about when they get older are their eyes, and I have found for years that sore or inflamed eyes are often deficient in Vitamin B_2.

I have told the story before and I must tell it again of how George Wright-Nooth, who was the second Chief of Police in Hong Kong, came to visit me. When he arrived he had a badly swollen eye, which was very red and inflamed, and I said to him jokingly: 'You look as if you've been in one of your riots in Hong Kong!'

'It is not the riots,' he said, 'but I've come to England to go to Moorfield's Eye Hospital. I've a swelling in my eye and the doctors abroad cannot help me.'

I gave him some Vitamin B$_2$, which I always take myself, and which is unfortunately only made in capsules containing 10 mg each. I advised him to take four or five right away and to continue to do so two or three times during the day.

He telephoned me two days later to say: 'You will not believe this, but there's no need now for me to go to Moorfield's after all – the swelling has gone!'

I first learnt about the tremendous effect of Vitamin B$_2$ when I had a secretary who kept complaining she felt as if she had grit or sand in her eye. Vitamin B$_2$ cleared it immediately.

The eye also needs Vitamin A, and there are some excellent capsules (available under the brand-name Eye Caps) which consist of exactly the right amount of Vitamin A, together with other vitamins, and if you take one in the morning, you may be quite certain your eyes will have everything they need during the day.

One other thing I find very effective.

We all have points in our body which, if you press them they feel tender, affect pain somewhere else. These are called Pressure Points, and there is in America what is almost a cult – in that they have a Chapel which they call the 'Church of Contact Healing' – who work on the Pressure Points of the body.

With regard to the eyes, if you press the ball of your thumb on each side of your nose exactly beneath the eyebrow, you will feel right next to the top of the nose the place that is tender. Do not be rough, but keep your thumbs firmly on the spot for some minutes, then move a fraction outwards and there is another spot on which you can do exactly the same thing.

This relieves the eyes if you are tired or have been straining them for a long time.

I often use the Pressure Points on the other parts of the body and have always found it extremely effective.

Most conditions can be helped by Contact Healing, and it has been used in treating a wide variety of ailments, including several that failed to respond to conventional methods.

Many elderly people find they have 'back trouble'. To help relieve the pain find the posterior fontanelle which is located at the back of the head in the centre, slightly above the crown. This is a very important spot and has to do with balancing the spiritual life energy between the pituitary and the pineal glands. Thence the energy travels down the spinal cord.

In order to show where to find all the Pressure Points I would need to use several diagrams, with explanations which would fill another book!

Ears

Many people all over the world write to me and say: 'I find it hard to keep my balance.'

This is one of the hazards of old age – that one does begin to feel a bit 'wobbly' on one's feet, and it can be a danger when one is using an escalator in shops or at airports.

One thing I know of, and have proved over and over again, is something that I introduced into the Health Movement many years ago and was a national sensation at the time.

I was told about a laboratory in Switzerland which was producing a product which was already selling a million bottles a year in Germany. I was so interested to see it for myself that I made the journey and for the first time met the charming, energetic Mr Frederick Pestalozzi.

He was the proprietor of Strath-Labor who were making Bio-Strath, and to my astonishment he told me that he had when a young man, been in a desperate way with Menière's Disease. It was a strange thing to hear, for Menière's Disease makes the person who has it tend to be unable to keep his balance and also to hear incessant noises in the ears; the condition is not always curable.

It was because he fought against the doctors' verdict that he started to manufacture Bio-Strath, and when I met him I am quite certain his hearing was so acute he could hear a bat squeak; he was married with a number of delightful children whose number has increased over the years.

I saw Bio-Strath being made in enormous vats containing yeast and having added to it a unique biological process producing a yeast elixir containing all kinds of vital substances. Needless to say, honey was one of them!

At that time I was not so interested as I am now in old age, but what impressed me enormously was the amazing effect of Bio-Strath on children, not only physically but mentally.

I learnt that Bio-Strath has been tried out in a school for backward children, and of course because it is quite nice to take, the children enjoyed drinking it. In this particular school there was a little girl who was genuinely mentally retarded, and all she could do was sit painting enormous black, rather menacing-looking birds. Because it made her happy, it was what she was allowed to do – but after she had been drinking the Bio-Strath, as all the other children did in the school, slowly the black birds grew smaller and smaller, and eventually they turned into butterflies.

I have seen pictures of this process and I can assure you it is very, very impressive indeed!

I brought Bio-Strath back to England, and it was introduced first by the *Daily Mail*. It is now available in the United States as well.

After that the public demanded it and the sales went up because everybody who bought a bottle went back for another. The demand was so enormous that the laboratory reserve had to be fitted with a new bottling plant so that 6,000 bottles could be filled and labelled every day. In the last count it was nearly 3,000 every hour!

A new and better strain of yeast was introduced to the product by Dr Strathmeyer, who was the originator of Bio-Strath, and when this new strain of yeast was first put into the vats it was so strong that it rose higher and higher until it overflowed not only over the vat, but to fill the whole laboratory!

Poor Mr Pestalozzi had to stay up all night stirring each vat every two hours to keep it under control!

It is said that 'a live body needs a live medicine' – and how true that is. His story certainly showed me how very much alive Bio-Strath is. Every year more herbs and plants are added to the original yeast, but I think the Bio-Strath Elixir is one of the best tonics for older people who are worried about their balance and their hearing.

The two really go together because behind the ears is where our brains lie.

Here I would like to add something very interesting that I was told very recently by Lady Mariotta Napier, who lives in Scotland and has three small children. She discovered how to prevent car sickness in children by such a simple method that it is extraordinary no one has ever thought of it before.

Before a child starts out on a car journey, put a piece of adhesive tape behind the ears, on the protruding bone behind which the organs of balance lie. It does not seem possible, but if that is done no child is sick in a car.

Since we learned this my two small grandchildren have been up and down to Scotland without one disaster on the way, and I have much older friends who have tried it because they too suffered from travel sickness.

I have not yet experimented with those who lose their balance, but it is certainly worth trying. After all, you have very little to lose, by using two small pieces of adhesive tape.

There are Bio-Strath formulas for all the circulatory diseases, rheumatism, and ailments of the heart, liver, kidneys and bladder. I have been waiting for

'One must maintain one's standards at any time in life. Curiosity, Romance and Beauty are essential – and the never-ceasing search for happiness.

My favourite day of the week is Monday. Keep your eye on the ball – the concentration that hard work brings will take you a long way.'

'The Empress of Style'. Special Consultant to the Metropolitan Museum in New York. Her Costume Exhibitions, the last being La Belle Epoque, *have broken all records in attendance and have exerted a major influence in current fashions and design.*

years for something to help treat such common disorders in older people as well as in those younger ones who get bladder upsets and chills.

That particular formula is certainly effective on everybody to whom I have given it, and so is the cough formula which is a joy for the long-suffering husband or wife who has to try to sleep in the same room as someone with a hacking cough.

Fragile Bones

My mother fractured her leg when she was 95, and so many elderly people fall down, as Margaret, Duchess of Argyll did recently. Although it didn't seem a very bad fall, she fractured her hip.

I am convinced that many of these things could be avoided if first one takes estrogen, and secondly Dolomite, available in the UK and the USA.

Dolomite is a special form of bone meal which comes from the Dolomite mountains, and I am very insistent that my sons take four tablets every day, as I do. This is because Dolomite straightens and stiffens the spine. When Lord Mountbatten was getting on for nearly 80, he was very worried because he thought he was getting round shouldered. He started to exercise. Now, I think exercises are excellent if you have time for them, but it is far easier to take Dolomite tablets, and when I had persuaded Lord Mountbatten to take four a day, I could see an improvement in his stature – and he was a very tall man – almost immediately.

Dolomite also helps to prevent 'Dowager's hump', which often develops in older women when they stick their heads forward, resulting in a permanent hump at the top of their backs. Such a condition is not only due to a lack of calcium but also to a protein deficiency.

To have a straight back in order to walk with dignity and grace, remember, you need protein every day and also Dolomite so that your spine does not begin to curve.

This is one more thing I must add about Dolomite, and that is that if any adult has a fracture or a broken bone, Dolomite speeds up the healing process and in many cases I have found takes away the pain.

The first man to whom I gave it was a carpenter who fell off the roof of a shed he was repairing. He was quite badly hurt and in great pain and the moment I gave him Dolomite he could hardly believe it but the pain was minimized to such an extent that he could forget about it, and he has always assured me that the doctors were astonished at how quickly he recovered.

The same applies to a number of other people and although I am fully prepared to believe that Dolomite speeds up the healing process, I save myself from proving it personally by taking Dolomite tablets every morning, and if I have any problem in sleeping, at night too!

Insomnia

I promised earlier in this book that I would tell you how to sleep, and it is so simple that I am afraid you might think it is almost too easy.

But I promise you that if you persevere and take it every night, in a week you will automatically sleep deeply and wake up in the morning feeling fresh and ready for work.

What I do is to mix two large teaspoonsful of honey with a teaspoonful of cider vinegar and a tumbler of water.

Stir until the honey is completely dissolved, then drink it with Dolomite tablets.

When you get into bed, press for a few minutes on the Pressure Point which induces sleep. This is at the top centre of your forehead – where you would have the point of a 'widow's peak' if you had one. It feels a little bit tender when you touch it, and immediately the pressure of your finger will start you yawning.

Keep your finger there for perhaps two minutes, and you will find, after yawning deeply and continuously, that you fall sleep.

Pains in the Head

Many older people tell me they get 'pains in the head', but they do not do anything about it; they are not certain what causes it, but they know it is very painful.

I am very sympathetic because I had sharp pains a little while ago, and I learnt it was because I had a rather weak artery on one side of my head and the blood was therefore not circulating as well as it should.

The pains in my head were not really a headache, then, but more like the throbbing of neuralgia.

I have found the best cure is Magnesium Phosphate, which is one of the marvellous Tissue Salts. Professor Schuessler, the homoeopath who first identified the 12 Tissue Salts in the 19th century, advised:

'Potassium Phosphate ("Kali. Phos.", No. 6): Taken regularly can help keep the elderly person mentally alert. It is a great nerve and brain remedy and can assist those suffering from sleeplessness due to nervousness.

'Magnesium Phosphate ("Mag. Phos", No. 8): This wards off cramps and neuralgic pains often associated with advancing years.'

Tissue Salts are some of the main ingredients of Homoeopathic Medicine, which has a very large following. They can be obtained in the UK or the USA.

The Queen always has a homoeopathic doctor, and I myself used to go to a homoeopath, Sir George Weir, for many, many years. He convinced me that Tissue Salts are of great importance in medicine, and because they are very easy to obtain, we are inclined to forget them. Nevertheless, there are different Tissue Salts for every sort of ailment.

A Harley Street doctor gave me Magnesium Phosphate which immediately helped the pains in my head, and he also gave me acupuncture which I found so effective that after one treatment I went for six months without having another pain.

Prostate Gland

It was the Americans who first became aware of the importance of Zinc.

For years I have had letters from men asking me how they can cope with the difficulty and discomforts of the prostate gland, and although I have had quite reasonable success in suggesting pollen in different forms, there is nothing in my opinion as effective as Zinc.

Every man past the age of 50 should be compelled to take a controlled dosage of Zinc: if he did, he would bless this very important mineral until the day he died. Zinc tablets are obtainable in all Healthfood Stores.

It is never too late to start and Zinc prevents and cures almost all prostate troubles, and at the same time it can be extremely useful for women.

Zinc gives a woman a pure white skin, and in many ways makes her look younger.

Too often, I think, we forget that in due measure minerals are just as important in keeping us strong and healthy as vitamins – and I am not certain that Zinc is not at the top of the list!

Rejuvenation

I have mentioned many new rejuvenation products, but one that has been hailed in America and Germany as the most effective is RNA. It is also the most expensive.

Dr Benjamin S. Frank of New York has suggested that RNA Biogenic Stimulus Injections can speed up the rate of cell replacement. Dr Frank also reports improvements in energy, well-being, smoothness and quality of the skin, and that some wrinkles and lines do disappear completely.

RNA has no side-effects, and besides RNA_{13}, which is the rejuvenating injection, there are others for slimming, ear and heart trouble, liver problems, viruses, and sexual difficulties. The injection for the latter is particularly effective.

The injections are available in America and England from doctors who specialize in them, and one can also obtain RNA Vitality Capsules. These, of course, take longer to work but are very good if you cannot afford the injections.

Skin

Dale Alexander, the American author of *Dry Skin and Common Sense,* persuaded me to take a spoonful of cod-liver oil in a small amount of milk every morning. The result is that the skin over my whole body is no longer dry.

Wrinkles are prevented and certainly softened by the cream I use, which is Ronald Hagman's Anti-Wrinkle Cream. I use this at night, and twice a week I put on *Celaton Neydin F crème. Among many other things, this is particularly good for wrinkles and crowsfeet and has an almost magical effect upon the face overnight.

See also what I say about Propolis under 'Duodenal Ulcer'.

Teeth

It is absolutely essential that you should not be deceived into believing that Fluoride will do your teeth any good; neither will it your children's.

Artificial Fluoride added to the water supply can be dangerous, especially to people who are potentially susceptible to kidney disease. Any doctor will tell you this is the truth.

What I believe is essential is that everyone should take Bone Meal for their teeth.

I had the most appallingly bad teeth when I was about 30, and they became much worse after the War when obviously I was not having the right food to strengthen them. They nearly all had stoppings in them, and I dreaded going to the dentist. Now, at the age of 82, I have no false teeth, and I very, very

*only available in Britain

seldom need to go to the dentist.

The reason for this is that I suddenly became aware of the dangers of Fluoride, and learnt at the same time what Professor Alred Äslander has demonstrated most successfully in Sweden – that the use of Bone Meal could produce perfect teeth.

He states that the real cause of dental decay is starvation of the teeth – It is primarily mineral-starved teeth which are attacked by caries – It is the enamel which counts, and if the enamel is perfectly nourished it is immune against decay.

He carried out an experiment in the poorest part of Sweden on children who all had decaying teeth. They were given Bone Meal tablets every day, and within two years, where 100 per cent of the children had suffered from dental caries, all had perfect teeth.

Bone Meal is obtainable in any Healthfood Store, and as I always say to people, they give it to their roses and forget that it is very important to themselves!

From the moment a baby is able to take hard food it is very wise to crush up a Bone Meal tablet and give it in a spoonful of honey. This will ensure your child will have perfect teeth all his or her life, and will certainly avoid the risks that come from artificial Fluoride.

The best form of Bone Meal is, I think, Dolomite which, as I have said previously, comes from the Dolomite mountains.

Nothing is uglier than stained, yellow teeth in old people, as usually results from smoking, and I certainly advise anyone who can afford it as they get older, to have their teeth capped, as do all the film stars and practically everybody else in America where people have wonderful teeth.

I also think that the best toothpaste in the world for keeping your teeth and your gums well and healthy is Sarakan. This comes from the 'Toothbrush Tree' in Africa, where the natives have had the secret handed down through the centuries. They use the stems of the plant and have found it a complete protection against soft, spongy gums which result in bad teeth.

It was many years ago that a resident British Army officer noticed the extraordinarily beautiful teeth of the inhabitants and found it was due to the use of this particular tree.

Now *Sarakan is available in British Healthfood Stores, and I certainly would not use any other toothpaste.

For ulcers in any part of the mouth there is nothing which heals quicker than Tincture of Propolis.

*not yet available in USA

Ulcers

So many old people, especially women, get leg ulcers which are very painful and very difficult to cure.

I am absolutely convinced that unless there is some bone malformation on a part of the body, or the patient has a growth, leg ulcers come originally from lack of vitamins.

My district nurse was telling me about two old people in the village whom she visited every other day to treat their leg ulcers. 'I'm so worried about them,' she said, 'because it is very painful and they are very brave about it, but I know how unpleasant it must be, and they were so happy together until these horrible ulcers started.'

'Have you tried honey on the ulcers themselves?' I asked.

She looked suprised and replied: 'Nobody has ever suggested it.'

'Well, try honey,' I said, 'and make them eat it. I will also give you some vitamins for them to take.'

Two weeks later she came to see me saying with excitement: 'You will hardly believe it, but their ulcers have practically gone!'

In other cases I have found that honey is not always as completely effective as that, yet it helps considerably and vitamins always make a difference.

Only the other day, just after I had been introduced to Selenium – which as I told you is a new product – my dear old maid who is 87 and has been with me for nearly 40 years, was stung by an insect on the leg. To our dismay it turned into a leg ulcer.

She had had them before and they had been cured by conventional treatments, but obviously the skin was delicate and she is prone to them.

She tried a cream which she had been given in the past, but I also persuaded her to take Selenium and to her astonishment and mine, the ulcer healed within a week without a scar!

This convinced me that Selenium was an even better healer than I believed it to be already, and now I recommend that everybody who has leg ulcers should try Selenium, and of course, honey!

BARBARA CARTLAND'S EXPERIENCE ON HEALTH

1930–1932
Studied Herbal Medicine with the famous Mrs Lyell of Culpepper.

1931–1933
A patient and a student of Dr Dengler of Baden Baden. First use of olive oil as an internal treatment of liver complaints, colitis and inflammation of the bowel.

1930–1937
Helped Lady Rhys-Williams giving Vitamin B for persistent miscarriages and malnutrition in the Distressed Areas.

Studied the first use of Vitamin E with brood mares and later barren women.

1935 onwards
Worked with Dr Pierre Lansel, first practitioner in England to give injections of Vitamin B and C. Followed his experiments with hormones for rejuvenation and the Niehans treatment of Cell Therapy. Studied with two eminent doctors the effect of oil injection on external Haemorrhoids.

Studied the nutritional condition in her brother Ronald Cartland's Parliamentary Constituency, the King's Norton Division of Birmingham, where there was malnutrition from low wages.

Practised Yoga exercises and breathing with the only white Yogi in the world. Wrote in a monthly magazine on the subject.

Studied nutrition in Montreal and did two lecture tours in lower Canada during which visited a large number of schools and hospitals.

1939–1945
County Cadet Officer for the St John Ambulance Brigade, Bedfordshire. Arranged First Aid and Home Nursing Lectures and discussed nutrition with doctors from overseas. Only Honorary Member of the Officers' Mess (doctors and psychiatrists) of 101 Convalescent Home, the largest Rehabilitation Centre in Great Britain.

Looked after 10,000 RAF and the crews of US Flying Fortresses until the American Red Cross arrived.

Studied nutrition of the troops and the conditions in the Prisoner-of-War Camps.

As Lady County Welfare Officer of Bedfordshire Voluntary Junior Commander (Captain) ATS, dealt with innumerable complaints over food from RAF Camps, Secret Stations and Searchlight Posts, and with the health and employment of pregnant mothers from all three Services. Studied conditions in hospitals treating women in the Armed Services.

1945
Was introduced in America to the first B-Complex Multi-Vitamin (synthetic) capsule. On return home was closely in touch with the American manufacturers of vitamins, receiving regular reports, literature and supplies until the Organic Vitamin Company opened Hemel Hempstead.

1950
Vitamins saved Barbara Cartland's life. Kept 52 farrowing sows on her farm in Hertfordshire and experimented by giving them and the boars Brewer's Yeast from a brewery. For four years

held the record production for Great Britain with an average of 11 a litter. Method copied by Sir Harry Haig for Ovaltine. Her prize-winning bull was given Vitamin E injections.

1955
Published: *Marriage for Moderns, Be Vivid Be Vital, Love, Life and Sex, Vitamins for Vitality.*

Began her lectures on Health.

Became a County Councillor for Hertfordshire, on Education and Health Committees for nine years.

Studied nutrition with regard to school meals. Deeply concerned with the health and conditions of Old People. Was so horrified at the way they were fed in some homes, and their general treatment, that her daughter – then Viscountess Lewisham – visited 250 homes all over Great Britain. Following her reports and Barbara Cartland's, and the tremendous press publicity involved, the Minister for Housing and Local Government (The Rt Hon. Duncan Sandys) instigated an enquiry into the 'Housing and Conditions of the Elderly'.

Was on the Managerial Committee of several old people's homes, and a Patron of Cell Barnes, the largest home for retarded children in Great Britain.

Visited and inspected innumerable hospitals, clinics and homes for the elderly and children. Started her fight for better salaries and conditions for midwives and nurses, which brought her into close contact with many of the teaching hospitals and the Royal College of Midwives.

1958
Was host to Professor Ana Aslan, founder of H3, on her first visit to England at the invitation of 400 doctors. Also tried acupuncture and the Cyriac Method of holding a slipped rib or disc.

1960
Started to write monthly for *Here's Health.*

Co-founder of the National Association for Health.

Answered 5,000 letters in a year (15,000 in 1984). *The Magic of Honey* (1 million copies) doubled the sale of honey in Great Britain and over the world.

Lectured on Health to:
    The Southgate Technical College
    The Queen Elizabeth College of
      Nutrition
    The Hertfordshire Police Cadets
    Two audiences of 2,500 in the
      Birmingham Town Hall
    Midwives, Universities, Rotary
      Clubs etc., frequently.

1964–1978
Given a Civic Reception by the Mayor of Vienna for her work in the Health Movement.

Had private discussions on Health, herbs and health foods with:
    The Ministers of Health and
    Sciences in Mexico, Japan and India.
    Professors and scientists in Mysore
    working on the development of
    agriculture in the famine areas near
    Kerala, with the India Ladies'
    Committee and Officials on Health
    in Bombay, New Delhi and Mysore.

In touch with the Indian Guild of Service working among orphans, and in the poor areas in India, and saw the conditions among the first three million Pakistanis who moved into Calcutta in 1958.

Visited the new refugee areas in Hong Kong, was the first woman to visit (with the police) the Chinese border, seeing the conditions of the workers.

Visited Nepal and saw the insanitary conditions in Katmandu and the rat-infested refuse in the streets. Discussed the conditions with officials.

Visited hospitals, clinics and old people's homes in many parts of India, Thailand, Hong Kong, Singapore, Switzerland, Austria and France.

Taken on a special visit with five doctors and scientists to inspect the Vitel Clinic in France.

Visited the slums of Delhi, Calcutta, Bombay, Phnom Penh (Cambodia), Taiwan, Singapore, Rio, Glasgow and London. Had talks with the leading doctor in Istanbul and was shown Clinical Trials undertaken.

Was closely in touch with the pioneers of the Health Movement in South Africa.

Invited to Yugoslavia, Germany and France.

1978
Visited Leningrad and Moscow and had talks with scientists on old age problems and the use of Ginseng.

1984
A Dame of Grace of St John of Jerusalem, Chairman of the St John Council, and Deputy President of the St John Ambulance Brigade Hertfordshire; one of the first women in 1,000 years to be on the Chapter General. President of the Hertfordshire Branch of the Royal College of Midwives. President of the National Association for Health.

Miss Cartland would like to thank Geraldine, Queen Mother of the Albanians; H.R.H. The Infanta Doña Marisol de Baviera e Borbón; Rosalynn Carter; H.M. Queen Farida of Egypt; Her Excellency Mrs Indira Gandhi; H.H. Princess Ayesha The Rajmata of Jaipur; The Princess Helena Moutafian, M.B.E.; Margaret, Duchess of Argyll; Rafaelle, Duchess of Leinster; Clare, Duchess of Sutherland; Dame Anna Neagle, C.B.E.; Sir John Mills, C.B.E.; Douglas Fairbanks, K.B.E.; Zsa Zsa Gabor; Helen Hayes; Cary Grant; Miss Deborah Kerr; Dorothy Lamour; Evelyn Laye; Margaret Lockwood; Robert Merrill; Norman Parkinson; Sylvia Sidney and Diana Vreeland for supplying photographs.
Photographs were also supplied by the following agencies: Keystone Press Agency 60, 157; Kobal Collection 81, 86, 95, 119, 126, 127, 141; Rex Features 29, 45, 48, 100, 137, 144, 177; Barry Swaebe 56.

The publishers would also like to thank Miss Cartland for permission to reproduce the black and white drawings of Francis Marshall, and artist Roger Hall for hand-tinting them.

Multimedia Publications have endeavoured to observe the legal requirements with regard to the rights of suppliers of photographic materials.

Mrs. Samuel Ramsey
404 Bartram Road
Willow Grove, PA 19090